RISING STARS
Maths

Problem Solving and Reasoning

Tim Handley and Chris Hutchinson

YEAR 2

Author Key Strategies: Tim Handley

Author Activities and Investigation: Chris Hutchinson

Consultant: Cherri Moseley

Publisher: Fiona Lazenby

Project Manager: Sarah Garbett

Editorial: Jan Fisher, Ethel Chitagu, Bruce Nicholson

Cover design: Words & Pictures Ltd

Design: Words & Pictures Ltd

Typesetting: Sg Creative Services

Illustrations: Tomek Giovanis

CD-ROM development: Alex Morris

British Library Cataloguing in Publication Data.
A CIP record for this book is available from the British Library.

ISBN: 978-1-78339-174-5

Printed by: Ashford Colour Press Ltd, Gosport, Hants

Acknowledgements

The authors and publishers would like to thank the staff and pupils at the following schools who trialled the *Problem Solving and Reasoning* resources and provided material for the Case Study conversation snippets across the series:

Bentley CEVC Primary School, Bentley, Ipswich
Bignold Primary School and Nursery, Norwich
Copdock Primary School, Copdock, Suffolk
Cutnall Green First School, Cutnall Green, Worcs
Delce Junior School, Rochester, Kent
Ditchingham Primary School, Ditchingham, Suffolk
Donington Cowley Endowed Primary School, Donington, Lincs
Eccleston C E Primary School, Chester, Cheshire
Garden Suburb Junior School, London
Gillingham ST Michael's Primary School, Gillingham, Beccles, Suffolk
Hapton CE VC Primary School, Hapton, Norwich
Harleston CEVA Primary School, Harleston, Norfolk
Piddle Valley CE VA First School, Piddletrenthide, Dorchester, Dorset
St Barnabas CE Primary, Warrington
St Francis de Sales Catholic Junior School, Walton, Liverpool
St Nicholas CE Primary, Hurst, Reading, Berkshire
St. Martha's Catholic Primary School, Kings Lynn, Norfolk
Well Lane Primary School, Birkenhead, Wirral
Woodlands Primary Academy, Great Yarmouth, Norfolk
Worfield Endowed Church of England Primary School, Worfield, Bridgnorth, Shropshire

First Mental Arithmetic 3

Schofield&Sims

Name _____

The Language of Maths

Add	+	more than, and, in total, altogether, plus
Subtract	−	take, less than, fewer than, take away, minus
Equals	=	makes, is

$$4 + 2 = 6$$
$$6 - 4 = 2$$

Pyramid   Cube   Sphere   Cuboid

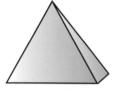 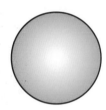 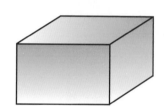

Turn   Half turn   Quarter turn

Measure

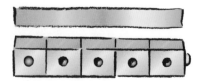 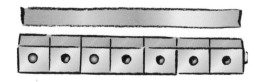

Contents

Section 1

A

1 Write the missing numbers.

| 14 | 15 | | | |

| 26 | 27 | | | |

2 Write the missing numbers.

| 11 | 12 | | 14 | | 16 | | 18 | | 20 |

3 Write the missing numbers.

| 11 | | 13 |

| 45 | | 47 |

B

4 Write how many tens there are. Write how many ones there are.

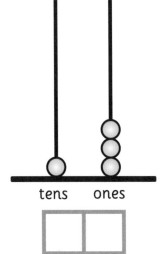

tens   ones

| | |

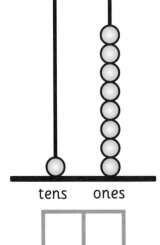

tens   ones

| | |

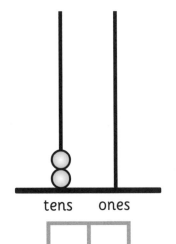

tens   ones

| | |

5 Draw lines to show where the numbers belong.

39   **36**   **34**

33						40

6 Write all the missing numbers.

10					15

52					57

15					20

C

7 Alfie has a bag of 10 toffees and 3 more toffees.
Show how many he has on this abacus.

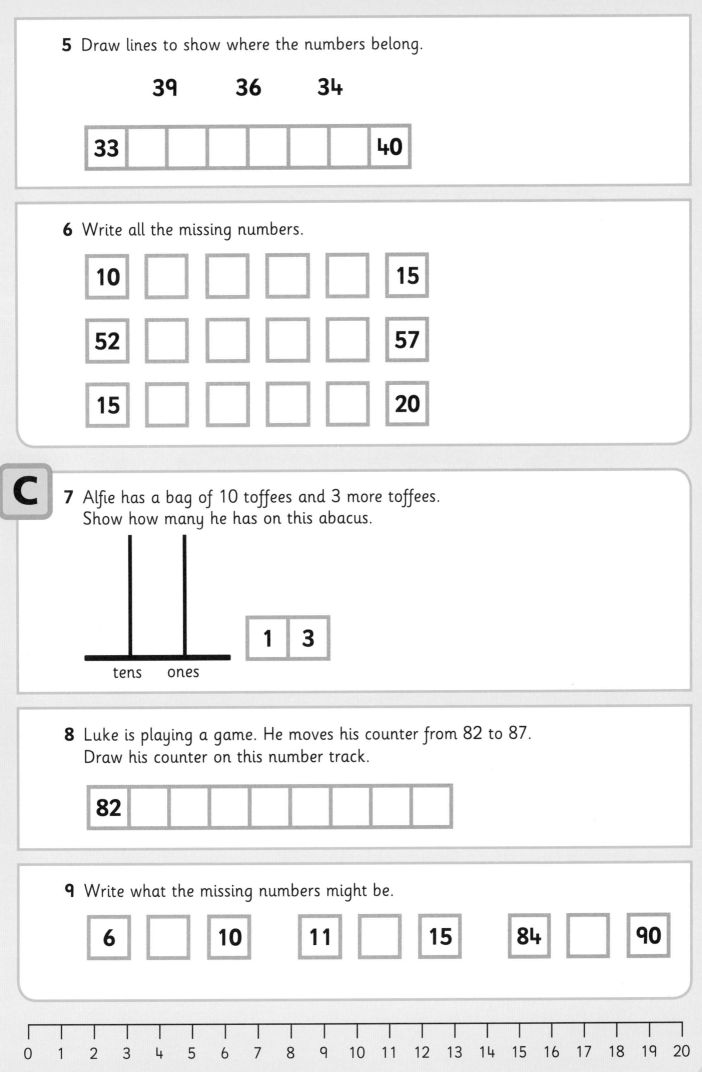

tens   ones

1	3

8 Luke is playing a game. He moves his counter from 82 to 87.
Draw his counter on this number track.

82								

9 Write what the missing numbers might be.

6		10		11		15		84		90

```
|--|--|--|--|--|--|--|--|--|--|--|--|--|--|--|--|--|--|--|--|
0  1  2  3  4  5  6  7  8  9  10 11 12 13 14 15 16 17 18 19 20
```

Section 1 Session 2

A

1 Find the missing numbers.

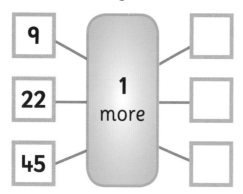

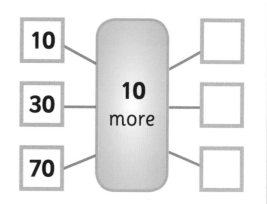

2 Start with the larger number. Count on to add. Write the total.

5 and **4** more

8 and **3** more

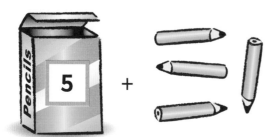

5 + ☐ = ☐

8 + ☐ = ☐

3 Find the difference by counting up from the smaller number.

 and ☐

 and 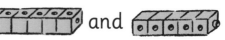 ☐

 and  ☐

B

4 Write the answers.

1 more than **12** is ☐

10 more than **40** is ☐

1 less than **27** is ☐

10 less than **30** is ☐

6

5 Write the answers in words.

Six add five is [   ]   Nine add four is [   ]

Three more than five is [   ]

6 Write the answers.

The difference between **4** and **3** is [ ]

The difference between **7** and **5** is [ ]

The difference between **10** and **5** is [ ]

C

7 Write the answer.

Amir has **18** sweets. Jake has **1** sweet fewer than Amir.

How many sweets does Jake have? [ ]

8 Write the answer.

There are **9** birds on the fence. **3** more birds come.

How many birds are there now? [ ]

9 Write the answer.

Freya has **8** grapes. Alice has **5** grapes.

How many more grapes does Freya have than Alice? [ ]

0 1 2 3 4 5 6 7 8 9 10 11 12 13 14 15 16 17 18 19 20

A

1 Find the difference.

2 Write the change.

3 Join pairs to make a total of 10.

| 6 | 9 | 3 | 8 | 5 | 0 |

| 1 | 2 | 5 | 4 | 10 | 7 |

B

4 Write the answers.

What is the difference between **6** and **4**?

What is the difference between **5** and **7**?

What is the difference between **9** and **4**?

5 Use a 20p coin each time. Write the answers.

I spend **7p**. What is my change? ☐ p

I spend **9p**. What is my change? ☐ p

I spend **4p**. How much change do I get? ☐ p

6 Write the missing numbers.

4 and **6** make ☐   ☐ and **7** is **10**

10 minus ☐ is **9**   **5** add ☐ equals **10**

C

7 Write the answer.

Eva has **8p**. Isabel has **3p**.

How much more money has Eva than Isabel? ☐ p

8 Write the answer.

I have **20p**. I buy a comic for **6p**.

How much change do I get? ☐ p

9 Write the answer.

Tom has **4p**. Paulo has **6p**.

How much money do they have in total? ☐ p

| 0 | 1 | 2 | 3 | 4 | 5 | 6 | 7 | 8 | 9 | 10 | 11 | 12 | 13 | 14 | 15 | 16 | 17 | 18 | 19 | 20 |

Section 1 Session 4

A

1 Join pairs that total 5.

2 Write the answers.

  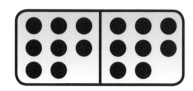

$6 + 6 =$ ☐ $7 + 7 =$ ☐ $8 + 8 =$ ☐

3 Write the differences.

$6 - 4 =$ ☐ $10 - 3 =$ ☐ $12 - 8 =$ ☐

B

4 Write the answers.

2 add **3** is ☐   **5** subtract **3** is ☐   **1** add **3** equals ☐

The difference between **4** and **2** is ☐

5 Write the answers.

Double **4** is [ ]   Double **5** is [ ]   **6** and **6** is [ ]

6 Write the answers.

The difference between **6** and **4** is [ ]

The difference between **8** and **5** is [ ]

The difference between **12** and **2** is [ ]

C

7 Write the answer.

Amber has **4** sweets. She eats **2** sweets.

How many sweets does Amber have left? [ ]

8 Write the answer.

Dad throws a dart. It lands on double **7**.

What is Dad's score? [ ]

9 Write the answer.

Sam has **9** marbles. Yousef has **7** marbles.

How many more marbles does Sam have than Yousef? [ ]

0 1 2 3 4 5 6 7 8 9 10 11 12 13 14 15 16 17 18 19 20

Section 1   Session 5

1 Tick the picture that belongs in the shaded box.

2 Sort the numbers into the boxes.

1   2   3   4   5   6   7   8   9   10

Odd	Even

3 Write the answers.

12 − 9 = ☐   19 − 7 = ☐   18 − 9 = ☐

4 Draw the other half of the picture.

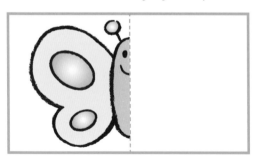

5 Circle the number that is in the wrong box.

Less than **10**	Not less than **10**
1 2 4 6 11	12 16 20 30 25

6 Write the answers.

The difference between **16** and **4** is ☐

17 take away **3** is ☐   **20** take away **8** is ☐

C   **7** Finish the picture.

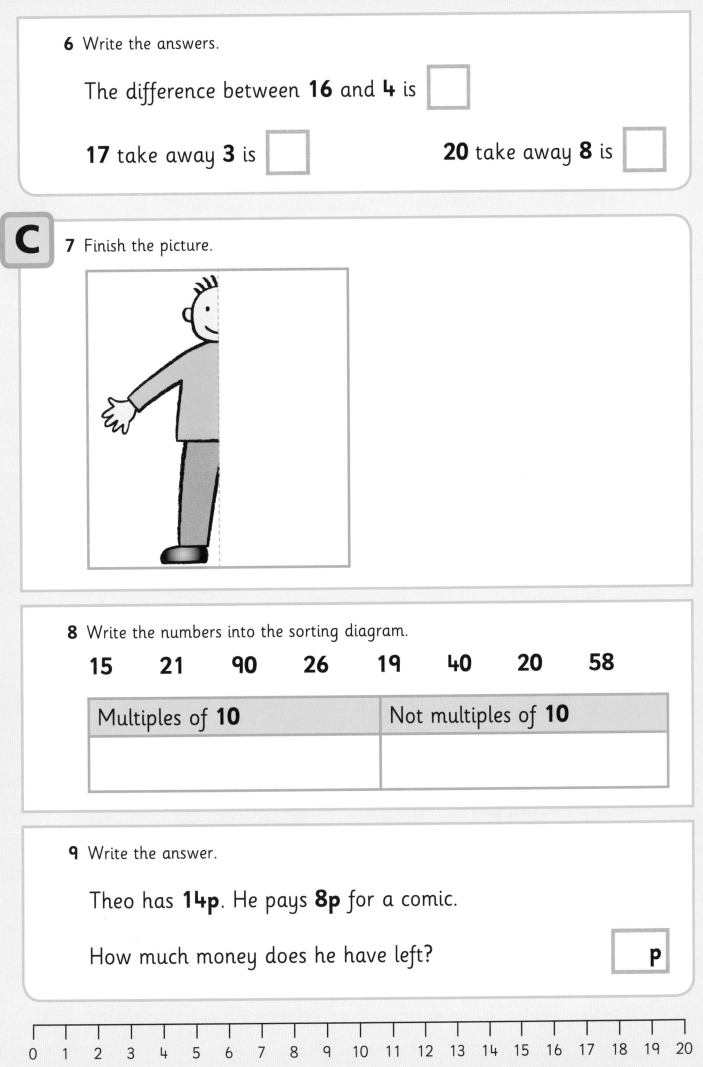

8 Write the numbers into the sorting diagram.

15   **21**   **90**   **26**   **19**   **40**   **20**   **58**

Multiples of **10**	Not multiples of **10**

9 Write the answer.

Theo has **14p**. He pays **8p** for a comic.

How much money does he have left?   ☐ **p**

0 1 2 3 4 5 6 7 8 9 10 11 12 13 14 15 16 17 18 19 20

Section 1 Check-up 1

1

1 Write the missing numbers.

8 | 9 | 10 | | | | |

2 Join the numbers to their place on the number line.

42 | 48 | 46 | 45 | 47

41   50

3 Write the missing number.

26 | | 28

4 Write the missing numbers.

10 less   **10** more

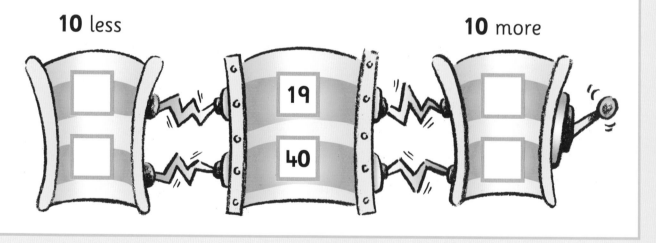

19

40

5 Write the answer.

Isaac has **8** muffins. Freddie has **11** muffins.

How many fewer muffins than Freddie does Isaac have?

6 Join numbers that total 10.

| 1 | 2 | 3 | 4 | 5 | 6 | 7 | 8 | 9 |

| 2 | 4 | 9 | 8 | 3 | 6 | 5 | 1 | 7 |

7 Write the answers.

$4 - 1 = \square$ $2 + 3 = \square$ $5 - 3 = \square$

8 Write the answers.

Double **6** is $\square$ $7 + 7 = \square$

9 Draw the rest of the picture.

10 Write the numbers into the sorting diagram.

15   21   30   16   18   31

Has the tens digit **1**	Does not have the tens digit **1**

0 1 2 3 4 5 6 7 8 9 10 11 12 13 14 15 16 17 18 19 20

15

Section 2

1 How long is the ribbon?

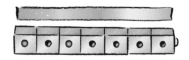

☐ blocks

2 Write the answer.

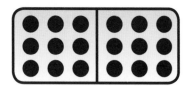

$9 + 9 =$ ☐

3 Write the answers.

$6 + 3 =$ ☐

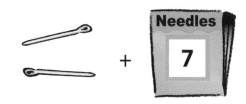

$2 + 7 =$ ☐

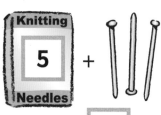

$5 + 3 =$ ☐

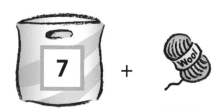

$7 + 1 =$ ☐

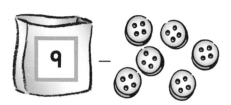

$9 - 6 =$ ☐

$8 - 7 =$ ☐

B

4 Write the answers.

Double **5** is ☐   Double **3** is ☐   Double **8** is ☐

5 Write the answer in words.

The ribbon is ten sticks long.

How long would two ribbons be? [____] sticks

6 Write the answers.

6 add **5** equals [ ]

11 take away **3** is [ ]

9 add **4** equals [ ]

12 subtract **2** leaves [ ]

The difference between **9** and **3** is [ ]

C

7 Write the answer.

The string is **6** metres long. Joel cuts off **4** metres of string.

How much string is left? [ ] metres

8 Write the answer.

Lucy has **£7**. Her dad gives her another **£7**.

How much money does Lucy have now? [£]

9 Write the answer.

There are **16** flowers in the vase. Isha takes out **5** flowers.

How many flowers are in the vase now? [ ]

| 0 | 1 | 2 | 3 | 4 | 5 | 6 | 7 | 8 | 9 | 10 | 11 | 12 | 13 | 14 | 15 | 16 | 17 | 18 | 19 | 20 |

Section 2 Session 2

A

1 Write the missing numbers.

2 Write the answers.

£5 + £5 + £5 = £ ☐

£10 + £10 + £10 + £10 = £ ☐

3 Share the flowers equally between the vases.

Write how many flowers there are in each vase.

B

4 Write the missing numbers.

| 10 | 15 | 20 | ☐ | ☐ | ☐ |

| 40 | 50 | ☐ | ☐ | 80 | 90 |

18

5 Write the answers.

2 and **2** and **2** and **2** is [ ]   **5** and **5** and **5** is [ ]

6 Use the pictures to help you.

10 shared by **2** is [ ]   **15** shared by **5** is [ ]

C

7 Write the answer.

Ava hops in **2s** from **0** along the number track.
She makes **4** hops.

What number does she land on? [ ]

8 Write the answer.

Dylan has **5** red apples and **5** green apples.

How many apples is that in total? [ ]

9 Write the answer.

Elliot has **6** oranges.
He shares the oranges equally between **3** plates.

How many oranges are there on each plate? [ ]

```
0  1  2  3  4  5  6  7  8  9  10  11  12  13  14  15  16  17  18  19  20
```

Section 2　Session 3

A

1 Draw the hands to show these times.

　　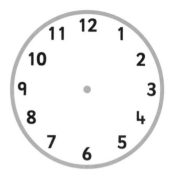

6.00　　　　　**1.30**　　　　　**9.30**

2 Write the answers.

6 + 7 = ☐　　　　　9 − 6 = ☐

3 Write the answers.

 − 5 = ☐　　　　 − 7 = ☐

B

4 Tick the clock that shows the earliest time.

afternoon　　　　　morning　　　　　evening

5 Write the answers.

8 add **2** equals ☐

10 subtract **4** leaves ☐

The difference between **9** and **5** is ☐

6 Write the answers.

19 subtract **7** is ☐

15 take away **3** leaves ☐

18 minus **6** equals ☐

13 subtract **4** leaves ☐

C

7 Write the answer.

Mum leaves home at **8** o'clock.
She gets to work **1** hour later.

At what time does she get to work? ☐ o'clock

8 Write the answer.

Toby has **£9**. His dad gives him another **£3**.

How much money does Toby have now? £ ☐

9 Write the answer.

There are **15** birds on the roof. **4** birds fly away.

How many birds are left on the roof? ☐

0 1 2 3 4 5 6 7 8 9 10 11 12 13 14 15 16 17 18 19 20

Section 2 Session 4

1 Tick things that turn.

2 Write the answers.

 +     **–**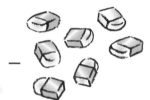

3 + 5 = ☐   **9 – 7 =** ☐

3 Write the answers.

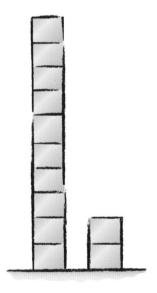   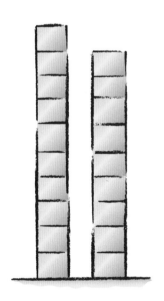   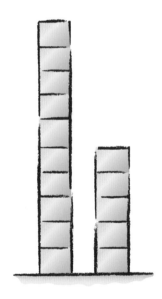

12 – 2 = ☐   **19 – 8 =** ☐   **15 – 3 =** ☐

B

4 Write the answers.

7 add **4** equals ☐   **9** and **2** is ☐

7 take away **3** is ☐   **8** minus **3** is ☐

22

5 Tick, circle or cross the answer.

Put a tick on the right-hand side of the picture.

Put a cross underneath the table.

Put a circle above the chair.

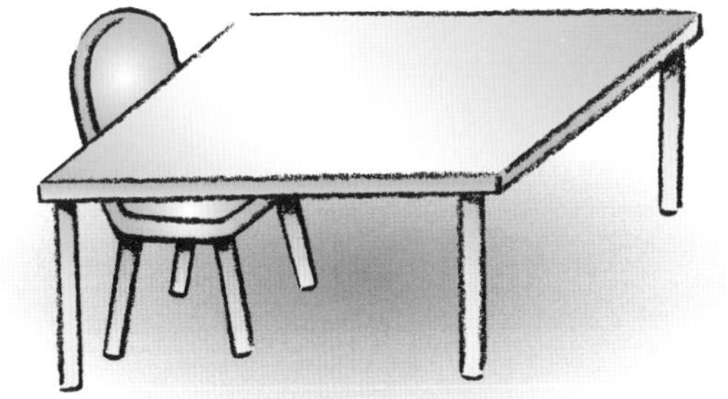

6 Write the answers in words.

Eighteen minus seven is

Nineteen subtract four is

C

7 Look at the picture for question 5.

Draw a plate on the table.

8 Write the answer.

Harry has
£2
and
£2
. Daniel has
£5
Bank of England
FIVE POUNDS
5
.

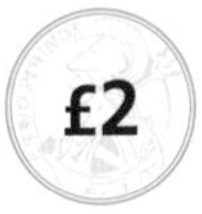

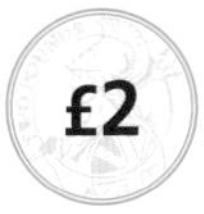

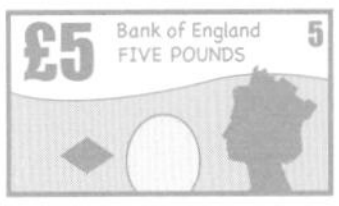

How much have Harry and Daniel in total? £

9 Write the answer.

There are **18** cows in the field.
The farmer puts **4** of the cows into the barn.

How many cows are left in the field?

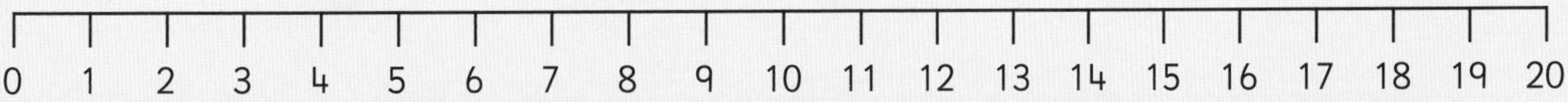

0 1 2 3 4 5 6 7 8 9 10 11 12 13 14 15 16 17 18 19 20

Section 2 Session 5

1 Draw a line on these shapes to cut them in half.

Now draw another line on the square to make quarters.

2 Put a tick on the right-hand side of the picture.

3 Write how much the coins total.

 and [ ] p   and [ ] £

 and [ ] p   5p and [ ] p

B

4 Write the answers.

Write what is half of 6.   Write what is a quarter of 4.

   [ ]    [ ]

5 Put a tick on the left-hand side of the picture.

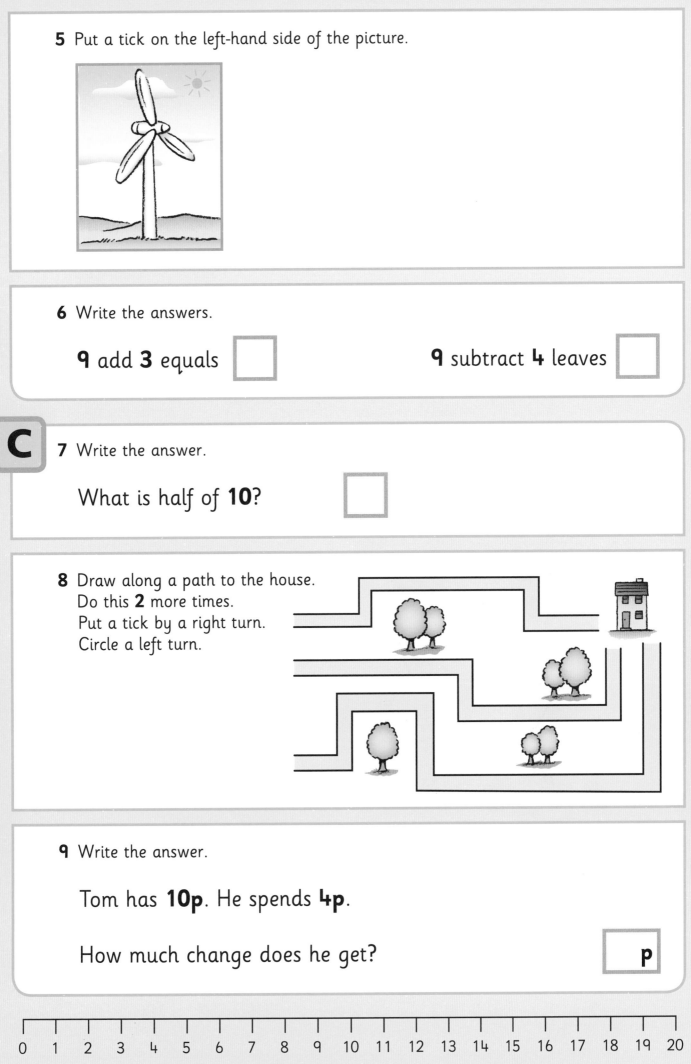

6 Write the answers.

9 add **3** equals ☐   **9** subtract **4** leaves ☐

C

7 Write the answer.

What is half of **10**?   ☐

8 Draw along a path to the house.
Do this **2** more times.
Put a tick by a right turn.
Circle a left turn.

9 Write the answer.

Tom has **10p**. He spends **4p**.

How much change does he get?   ☐ **p**

```
|   |   |   |   |   |   |   |   |   |   |   |   |   |   |   |   |   |   |   |   |
0   1   2   3   4   5   6   7   8   9   10  11  12  13  14  15  16  17  18  19  20
```

Section 2

A

1 Count the flowers. Write how many.

2 Share the flowers into the vases. Write how many there are in each vase.

3 Write the answers.

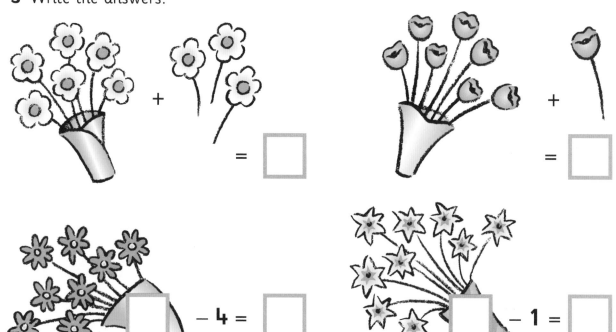

+ = ☐

+ = ☐

☐ − 4 = ☐

☐ − 1 = ☐

B

4 Write the answers.

2 + 2 + 2 + 2 + 2 = ☐   10 + 10 + 10 + 10 = ☐

5 Use the picture to help you.

10 shared by **2** is ⬜   10 shared by **5** is ⬜

6 Write the answers.

5 add **6** is ⬜   **3** add **4** is ⬜   **9** minus **4** leaves ⬜

The difference between **8** and **6** is ⬜

C

7 Write the answer.

Ruby has **5** red apples, **5** green apples and **5** yellow apples.

How many apples is that in total? ⬜

8 Write the answer.

Max has **10** apples.
He shares the apples equally between two plates.

How many apples are on each plate? ⬜

9 Write the answer.

9 birds sit on the wall. **7** birds fly away.

How many birds are on the wall now? ⬜

0 1 2 3 4 5 6 7 8 9 10 11 12 13 14 15 16 17 18 19 20

Section 2 Check-up 2

2

1 Write the answer.

$9 + 9 =$ ⬜

2 Write the answer.

$9 - 6 =$ ⬜

3 Write the missing numbers.

40	42	44			

4 Write the answer.

$2 + 2 + 2 + 2 + 2 + 2 =$ ⬜

5 Share the cakes equally onto the plates.
Write how many cakes there are on each plate.

⬜

6 Write how much the coins total.

 and £ ⬜   and ⬜ p

7 Write the answers.

Half of **6** is ⬜   Quarter of **8** is ⬜

28

8 Write the answer.

Erin's castle is **10** bricks high.
Katie's castle is **7** bricks high.

How much taller is Erin's castle
than Katie's castle?

☐ bricks

9 Draw the hands on the clocks.

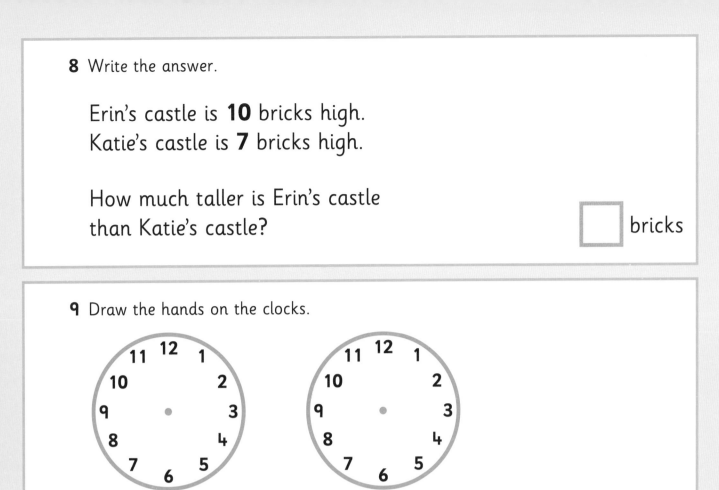

7 o'clock

Half past **1**

2 o'clock

Half past **5**

10 Tick the one that turns.

0 1 2 3 4 5 6 7 8 9 10 11 12 13 14 15 16 17 18 19 20

Check-up 3 Number

3

1 Write the missing numbers.

15 | 16 | 17

2 Write the missing numbers.

12 | 13 | | | | 17

3 Write the answers.

| **1** less | | **1** more | | **10** less | | **10** more |

□ — 16 — □   □ — 60 — □

4 Count on from the larger number to find the answer.

3 + 5 = □

5 Write the answers.

4 + 1 = □   5 − 3 = □

6 Write the answers.

7 + 7 = □   □ + 4 = 10

7 Write the missing number.

75 | | 77

8 Write the answers.

$1 + 8 =$ ☐　　　$9 - 4 =$ ☐

9 Write the missing numbers.

| 6 | 8 | 10 | ☐ | 14 |

| 30 | 35 | 40 | ☐ | 50 |

| 0 | 10 | 20 | ☐ | 40 |

10 Write the answers.

$2 + 2 + 2 =$ ☐　　$5 + 5 + 5 + 5 =$ ☐　　$10 + 10 =$ ☐

11 Share the cakes equally. Write how many are on each plate.

　　　☐

12 Write the answer.

$15 - 6 =$ ☐

13 Write the answers.

What is half of **8**? ☐　　　What is a quarter of **8**? ☐

0　1　2　3　4　5　6　7　8　9　10　11　12　13　14　15　16　17　18　19　20

Schofield & Sims

the long-established educational publisher specialising in maths, English and science

First Mental Arithmetic provides rich and varied practice to meet the requirements of the National Curriculum for primary mathematics. Questions in **First Mental Arithmetic 3** cover the key subject areas of number, measurement and geometry, including addition, subtraction, symmetry, length, doubles, halves, quarters and word problems. The accompanying answer book, **First Mental Arithmetic 3 Answers**, contains answers to all the questions included in **First Mental Arithmetic 3**.

First Mental Arithmetic comprises six one-per-child pupil books with accompanying answer books, as well as a single Teacher's Guide. The series develops children's essential maths skills and prepares them for the Key Stage 1 national tests. It reinforces maths vocabulary and provides intensive practice, encouraging children to monitor their own progress. All the books can be used flexibly for individual, paired, group or whole-class maths practice, as well as for homework and one-to-one intervention.

Structured according to ability rather than age, the series allows children to work at their own pace, building confidence and fluency. Two **Entry Tests** are available in the **First Mental Arithmetic Teacher's Guide** and on the Schofield & Sims website, enabling teachers, parents and tutors to select the appropriate book for each child.

First Mental Arithmetic 3 contains:
* 11 single-spread sessions, each comprising the following three parts
  Part A: questions using pictures or simplified language
  Part B: questions using relevant mathematical vocabulary and symbols
  Part C: word problems or questions that test understanding of mathematical concepts
* **Check-up Tests** to identify any gaps in understanding.

First Mental Arithmetic 1 978 07217 1163 8	**First Mental Arithmetic 1 Answers** 978 07217 1169 0
First Mental Arithmetic 2 978 07217 1164 5	**First Mental Arithmetic 2 Answers** 978 07217 1170 6
First Mental Arithmetic 3 978 07217 1165 2	**First Mental Arithmetic 3 Answers** 978 07217 1171 3
First Mental Arithmetic 4 978 07217 1166 9	**First Mental Arithmetic 4 Answers** 978 07217 1172 0
First Mental Arithmetic 5 978 07217 1167 6	**First Mental Arithmetic 5 Answers** 978 07217 1173 7
First Mental Arithmetic 6 978 07217 1168 3	**First Mental Arithmetic 6 Answers** 978 07217 1174 4
First Mental Arithmetic Teacher's Guide 978 07217 1210 9	

Mental Arithmetic is available for older pupils

First edition published in 2011. This edition copyright © Schofield & Sims Ltd, 2016. Second impression 2016.
Author: Ann Montague-Smith. Ann Montague-Smith has asserted her moral right under the Copyright, Designs and Patents Act, 1988, to be identified as the author of this work.
British Library Cataloguing in Publication Data. A catalogue record for this book is available from the British Library.
All rights reserved. Except where otherwise indicated, no part of this publication may be reproduced, stored in a retrieval system, or transmitted in any form or by any means, electronic, mechanical, photocopying, recording or otherwise, without either the prior permission of the publisher or a licence permitting restricted copying in the United Kingdom issued by the Copyright Licensing Agency Limited, Saffron House, 6–10 Kirby Street, London EC1N 8TS.
Design by Ledgard Jepson Ltd. Front cover design by Peter Grundy. Printed in the UK by Page Bros (Norwich) Ltd.

Mental Arithmetic

MIX
Paper from responsible sources
FSC® C023114

ISBN 978-07217-1165-2

9 780721 711652

ISBN 978 07217 1165 2
Key Stage 1
Age range 5–7+ years
£3.50 (Retail price)

For further information and to place your order visit
www.schofieldandsims.co.uk or telephone 01484 607080

Contents

Introduction

Rising Stars Maths *Problem Solving and Reasoning*

This resource is designed to help teachers develop a 'reasoning classroom' where problem solving and reasoning forms an integral part of each maths lesson. It provides key strategies to help teachers achieve this, together with extended investigation activities.

Problem solving and reasoning in the 2014 curriculum

The aims of the 2014 National Curriculum for Mathematics place a significant emphasis on the development of children's problem-solving and reasoning skills. Below are the aims of the curriculum, with the key elements relating to problem solving and reasoning underlined.

"The national curriculum for mathematics aims to ensure that all pupils:

- become **fluent** in the fundamentals of mathematics, including through varied and frequent practice with increasingly complex problems over time, so that pupils develop conceptual understanding and the ability to recall and apply knowledge rapidly and accurately.

- **reason mathematically** by following a line of enquiry, conjecturing relationships and generalisations, and developing an argument, justification or proof using mathematical language

- can **solve problem**s by applying their mathematics to a variety of routine and non-routine problems with increasing sophistication, including breaking down problems into a series of simpler steps and persevering in seeking solutions.

Mathematics is an interconnected subject in which pupils need to be able to move fluently between representations of mathematical ideas. The programmes of study are, by necessity, organised into apparently distinct domains, but pupils should make rich connections across mathematical ideas to develop fluency, mathematical reasoning and competence in solving increasingly sophisticated problems."

These aims extend problem solving and reasoning beyond simple worded problems, and it is expected that they will form a key part of the new statutory assessments at both KS1 and KS2.

Within the Programmes of Study, very few statements specifically related to problem solving and reasoning statements are provided. To help teachers develop a range of problem solving skills, suggested objectives have been developed and are provided on pages 14 and 15. For this reason, it is important that, when planning maths lessons, teachers always keep the aims of the curriculum in mind and incorporate problem-solving and reasoning opportunities into every lesson.

About the author

Tim Handley

Tim is the Mathematics and ICT Subject Leader at Woodlands Primary Academy, Great Yarmouth, Norfolk and is a Mathematics Specialist Teacher. He is also an accredited NCETM Professional Development Lead (Primary) – one of only a handful of classroom teachers with this status. He has a deep-seated passion for ensuring all children develop a true conceptual understanding of mathematics.

The publishers and authors would like to thank the children and staff at Woodlands Primary Academy for their support in developing these resources

Chris Hutchinson

Chris is a Senior Teacher and Subject Leader for Maths at Lionwood Infant and Nursery School in Norwich, and is a Mathematics Specialist Teacher and Specialist Leader of Education for Mathematics. He is passionate about helping children to develop their own conceptual understanding through manipulating representations and providing opportunities for self-initiated learning.

How to use the resources

Structure

The resource is split into two sections:

1 *Key strategies*

2 *Activities and investigations*

At the back of the book you will also find a glossary of useful mathematical terms. All the supporting resources, including editable PowerPoint problem posters and Word files of the Resource Sheets can be found on the CD-ROM that accompanies this Teacher's Book.

Key strategies

This section provides 14 constructs or routines which can be used to integrate problem solving and reasoning into every maths lesson. Each Key Strategy is accompanied by a full explanation, tips for its use and a number of different examples of how the strategy could be used in different areas of mathematics to develop reasoning.

The examples provided are drawn from many areas of the mathematics curriculum. They are intended as starting points, which can then be taken and developed to use in all areas of mathematics.

Each strategy also contains a conversation snippet from a case study from the schools where these resources have been trialled.

Note that the content of some examples is pitched slightly below the equivalent year content objectives in the Programme of Study. This is to allow children to focus on the development of their **reasoning skills**, using subject knowledge with which they are already familiar.

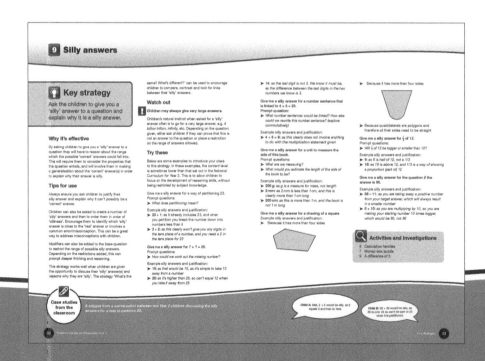

Activities and investigations

This section provides 18 extended problem-solving activities. These all develop one or more key problem-solving and reasoning skills, as well as, covering an area of the 2014 National Curriculum. Each activity will last a minimum of one hour and can in many cases, be developed further. The resources for each activity comprise:

- A poster to display on the interactive whiteboard to introduce the problem to the children. This includes the background to the problem, the main challenge or challenges, plus 'Things to think about' prompts to help develop children's reasoning skills. Where appropriate, definitions of any key mathematical terms are also included. Full colour versions of the posters can be found on the accompanying CD-ROM as editable PowerPoint files. They are also reproduced in The problem section of the teacher guidance for ease of reference. Some of the PowerPoint presentations include additional poster slides that can be used to aid differentiation by providing easier and harder versions of the problem.

- Detailed teacher guidance, which includes a learning objective, curriculum links, background knowledge and a step-by-step teaching sequence. The guidance also provides key questions to help develop reasoning (which use one of more of the Key Strategies). Ideas of how to adapt the activity for those that require further support and how the activity could be extended to meet the needs of more able mathematicians are also included.

- For some of the problems, additional Resource sheets that may be useful for the problem are provided on the CD-ROM.

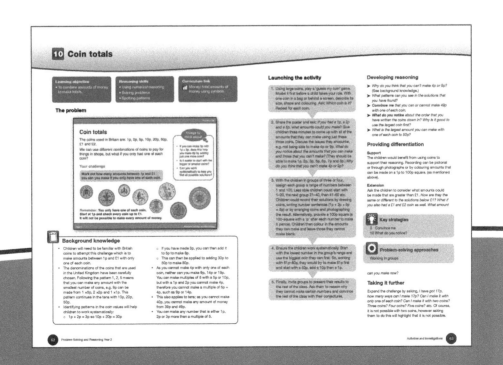

Maths superpowers CPD

John Mason[1] has identified a set of 8 'Mathematical Powers' that all children possess and which we need to foster and develop in order to create 'able mathematicians' who are able to reason about maths and problem solve. The powers, which come in pairs, are as follows:

Conjecture

Children should be encouraged to **make conjectures**, that is say what they think about what they notice or why something happens. For example, a conjecture made by a child could be, 'I think that when you multiply an odd number by an even number you are always going to end up with an even number'.

and

Convince

Children should then be encouraged to **convince**, that is to persuade people (a partner, group, class, you, an adult at home, etc.) that their conjectures are true. In the process of convincing, children may use some, or all, of their other 'maths powers'.

Organise

Children should be encouraged to **organise**, putting things (numbers, facts, patterns, shapes) into groups, in an order or a pattern, e.g. sorting numbers or shapes.

and

Classify

Children should then be encouraged to **classify** the objects they have organised, e.g. identifying the groups as odd and even numbers, irregular and regular shapes, etc.

Imagine

Children should be encouraged to imagine objects, patterns, numbers and resources to help them solve problems and reason about mathematics.

and

Express

Children should be encouraged to **express their thinking**, that is to show and explain their thinking and reasoning, e.g. about a problem, relationship or generalisations.

Specialise

Children should be encouraged to **specialise**, that is to look at specific examples or a small set of examples of something. For example, looking at the odd number 7 and the even number 8 to test their conjecture that an odd X even number = odd number. Children can also specialise in order to start to see patterns and relationships and make generalisations.

and

Generalise

Children should be encouraged to **generalise**, that is to make connections and use these to form rules and patterns. For example, from their specific example they could generalise that any odd number multiplied by any even number gives an even number. Children should also be encouraged to use algebra to express their generalisations.

These 'maths superpowers' have become the central foundation of many maths teacher development programmes, including the Mathematics Specialist Teacher (MaST) programme.

[1] Mason, J. and Johnston-Wilder,S (eds) (2004 a) Learners Powers in: *Fundamental Constructs in Education*, London:Routledge Falmer pp 115-142

8   Problem Solving and Reasoning Year 2

Developing reasoning

Reasoning and conceptual understanding

Encouraging children to reason in maths helps to support children to develop a conceptual and relational understanding of maths: an understanding of **why** maths 'works', rather than just following a set of instructions. This leads to a far greater understanding and confidence in maths.

Developing a reasoning classroom

1   Initially begin by choosing a few of the *Key Strategies* provided in the first section of this resource and introducing them to your class. Many of these strategies, such as **Always, sometimes, never, Peculiar, obvious, general** and **What's the same? What's different?** can also be extended to form whole lessons in their own right, which may be useful when children first experience the strategy.

2   Allow the strategies to form part of your day-to-day questioning, so that children become familiar with using them. If these routines are used regularly, children will quickly get used to structuring their thoughts in this way.

3   Then begin to use the extended problems in the *Activities and Investigations* section. These provide opportunities for children to develop their reasoning skills over a prolonged activity. Each activity includes suggestions of how the *Key Strategies* could be incorporated to develop children's thinking as they work on the investigations.

Cross-curricular reasoning

Of course, children's natural ability to reason extends beyond mathematics. *The Key Strategies* and approaches explained in this resource can easily be used across the curriculum. For example, in a geography-based lesson the question *What's the same and what's different about these two settlements?* could be asked. Alternatively, in an English lesson children could be asked to identify the **Odd one out** of a selection of words.

Problem-solving techniques

The following offers a number of suggestions that are useful to consider when organising and supporting children to encourage reasoning in the classroom.

USE ME

When supporting children in problem solving and reasoning activities, the following stages, which form the 'USE ME' mnemonic are useful to follow.

- **Understanding:** Check that children understand the problem, activity or statement that has been given. Does it need re-wording or further explanation? Do they have the subject knowledge needed?

- **Specialising:** Start by asking children to specialise by looking at, or creating, one specific example. This then can be extended to looking at/creating a small group of examples. By specialising, children are more likely to be able to explore the structure of the mathematics, before widening out to make connections and generalisations.

- **Encouraging representations:** The use of representations is vital as they significantly enhance children's experience and understanding of mathematics. Representations can take many forms including Practical (apparatus such as bead strings, counters, cubes, etc), Recording/Jottings (such as number lines) and Internal (internalised versions of representations that children visualise and imagine). Children should also be encouraged to create their own representations. Encourage children to think about how they could represent the statement, or how they could represent specific examples of the statement.

- **Making generalisations:** After children have looked at, and often represented, specialised examples, they can begin to explore the connections between their examples. Can they make a statement that applies to all examples? If no generalised statement is possible, can they make a statement that applies to some examples (and define which examples this applies to)? Can they explain why it is not possible to make a generalisation?

- **Extending:** Provide a further, linked, question or investigation for children to explore.

Grouping for problem solving and reasoning

Teachers often ask how it is best to group children for problem solving and reasoning tasks. Variety is really the key here! Below are some forms of groups for you to consider:

- **Familiar maths partners** who children work with frequently in maths and with whom they are able to communicate well.

- **Pairs of friends** who enjoy working together.

- **Mixed-ability pairs or groups** which have often been shown to raise attainment for all children in the group: the lower-attaining children benefit from the peer coaching from the higher-attaining children, whilst the higher-attaining children have to extend their understanding and thinking further in order to explain it clearly to others.

- **Same-ability pairs or groups** also, of course, have their place, as they allow the task to be closely matched to the children's ability

It is important that children become used to working in different types of groups. In this way, they develop increasing flexibility and become adept at explaining their thinking and reasoning to a wide range of people. Different tasks will, of course, suit different ways of grouping.

Panic envelopes to facilitate self-differentiation

These are a great strategy to enable self-differentiation of problem-solving and reasoning activities. Inside an envelope, place one or more items that will support the children in carrying out the activity, then place the envelopes either in the middle of a group's table and/or on a maths working wall.

The content of the envelopes can be varied, and could include:

- Additional information

- Key questions to help develop thinking

- Conjectures for the children to prove/disprove

- Specific examples

- Partly or fully worked solutions to part of the problem

Give children the challenge of taking part in the activity independently, but let them know that at any point during the activity they can self-select to open the panic envelope and read one or more of the items that you have placed inside. Of course, adults in the classroom can also suggest to children that they may benefit from opening the 'panic envelope' if they become stuck while working through an activity. The content of the envelopes can be further differentiated for different groups of children.

Graffiti maths

Graffiti maths is an approach to problem solving and reasoning tasks which encourages children to think and work 'big'. It was developed almost simultaneously by a number of teachers, including Claire Lotriet and Geoff Barton in 2012 .

Graffiti maths involves children working together as a team on a problem or investigation, working on tables that are covered in 'magic whiteboard' sheets, large pieces of paper (taped down) or another covering which allows children to write 'on' the tables. Some teachers also choose to remove the chairs from the classroom, which encourages children to move around the table.

This approach encourages children to work together and gives them ample space to explore ideas, test out conjectures and make connections. The recording space is shared, which means that one child is less likely to take 'ownership' of it whilst others hang back and 'lurk' in the background. The act of sharing the recording space also encourages maths talk and creates a generally 'buzzy' atmosphere in your classroom.

Children can also move around and look at different tables and their recording, which can be a very useful plenary or mid-session activity.

Think, pair, share

This strategy is particularly effective during shared learning. This is a development of 'simple' paired talk. Ask a question (usually open-ended) and give children a period of thinking time (normally one to two minutes works best) for them to 'privately' think about the question or problem posed. Next, give children some time to discuss the question/thinking with a partner, before the partners share their thinking with another pair (so forming groups of four).

Envoy

This technique enables ideas to be shared between different groups. Having given children time to discuss their own thoughts, conjectures and generalisations in groups, each group then sends an 'envoy' to share their discussions with another group.

The envoy could be chosen by the group, or be selected by the teacher. By randomly selecting the envoy, you will help each group ensure that every child in the group understands the thinking, conjectures or generalisations of the group as any one of them may be called upon to explain them to another group.

As a further extension, the envoy can be asked to bring back a summary of the thoughts from the group they visited to their 'Home' group, so that the groups can consider new ideas and revisit their own thinking in light of the other conjectures.

2 http://clairelotriet.com/blog/2012/12/15/graffiti-maths/

Snowballing

After giving time for paired discussion, the discussion can then be 'snowballed'. Ask pairs to share with another pair, and then these groups to snowball together and discuss with another group (forming groups of 8). Depending on class size, this can be repeated again (forming groups of 16) before each of the 'snowballed' groups feeds back to the whole class.

WWW and EBI as a plenary

A useful activity for the plenary session is to ask children **W**hat **W**ent **W**ell (WWW) about the activity and what would be **E**ven **B**etter **I**f (EBI). A ratio of 4 WWWs to 1 EBI is often effective, as this encourages children to focus on the positive and strengths from the session. The phrase of 'even better if ...' encourages children to be constructive in their suggestions for improvement. So, rather than 'we didn't work together very well', children might phrase an EBI as 'It would have been **even better if** we had listened more to what each other said so that we could share our thinking together.'

Assessing progress

Accurate assessment of children's problem solving and reasoning skills is only possible through observation of and conversations with the child, together with evidence from their recorded work. The bank of evidence of a child's problem solving and reasoning ability will naturally be built up over time, as children experience and take part in a range of different activities.

The objectives in the chart on the following pages can be used when planning and assessing the problem-solving and reasoning elements of the new curriculum.

Problem-solving and reasoning objectives

Year 1	Year 2	Year 3
• Describe a puzzle or problem using numbers, practical materials and diagrams; use these to solve the problem and set the solution in the original context. • Order and arrange combinations of objects and shapes in patterns. • Answer a question by selecting and using suitable equipment, and sorting information, shapes or objects; display results using tables and pictures. • Describe simple patterns and relationships involving numbers or shapes; decide whether examples satisfy given conditions. • Describe ways of solving puzzles and problems, explaining choices and decisions orally or using pictures.	• Identify and record the information or calculation needed to solve a puzzle or problem; carry out the steps or calculations and check the solution in the context of the problem. • Follow a line of enquiry; answer questions by choosing and using suitable equipment and selecting, organising and presenting information in lists, tables and simple diagrams. • Describe patterns and relationships involving numbers or shapes, make predictions and test these with examples. • Present solutions to puzzles and problems in an organised way; explain decisions, methods and results in pictorial, spoken or written form, using mathematical language and number sentences.	• Represent the information in a puzzle or problem using numbers, images or diagrams; use these to find a solution and present it in context, where appropriate using £.p notation or units of measure. • Follow a line of enquiry by deciding what information is important; make and use lists, tables and graphs to organise and interpret the information. • Identify patterns and relationships involving numbers or shapes, and use these to solve problems. • Express the rules for sequences in words (e.g. 3, 5, 7: you add 2 each time). • Begin to make generalisations based on patterns in mathematics (e.g. all even numbers end in either a 0, 2, 4, 6 or 8). • Begin to make conjectures (statements) about mathematics and develop the ability to convince others (e.g. when continuing a pattern). • Begin to make 'if...then...' statements (e.g. if 2 + 4 = 6 then 6 − 2 = 4). • Describe and explain methods, choices and solutions to puzzles and problems, orally and in writing, using pictures and diagrams.

Year 4	Year 5	Year 6
• Represent a puzzle or problem using number sentences, statements or diagrams; use these to solve the problem; present and interpret the solution in the context of the problem.	• Represent a puzzle or problem by identifying and recording the information or calculations needed to solve it; find possible solutions and confirm them in the context of the problem.	• Tabulate systematically the information in a problem or puzzle; identify and record the steps or calculations needed to solve it, using symbols where appropriate; interpret solutions in the original context and check their accuracy.
• Suggest a line of enquiry and the strategy needed to follow it; collect, organise and interpret selected information to find answers.	• Plan and pursue an enquiry; present evidence by collecting, organising and interpreting information; suggest extensions to the enquiry.	• Suggest, plan and develop lines of enquiry; collect, organise and represent information, interpret results and review methods; identify and answer related questions.
• Identify and use patterns, relationships and properties of numbers or shapes; investigate a statement involving numbers and test it with examples.	• Explore patterns, properties and relationships and propose a general statement involving numbers or shapes; identify examples for which the statement is true or false.	• Represent and interpret sequences, patterns and relationships involving numbers and shapes; suggest and test hypotheses; construct and use simple expressions and formulae in words then symbols.
• Express the rules for increasingly complex sequences in words (e.g. 3, 6, 12, 24: you double each time).	• Explain reasoning using diagrams, graphs and text; refine ways of recording using images and symbols.	• Explain reasoning and conclusions, using words, symbols or diagrams as appropriate. Use simple formulae expressed in words. Express missing number problems algebraically (e.g. $6 + n = 28$).
• Report solutions to puzzles and problems, giving explanations and reasoning orally and in writing, using diagrams and symbols.	• Begin to express missing number problems algebraically. (e.g. $6 + n = 12$).	• Begin to use symbols and letters to represent variables (things that can change) and unknowns in mathematics situations which they already understand, such as missing numbers, missing lengths, arithmetical rules (e.g. $a + b = b + a$) and number puzzles (e.g. two numbers total 6, therefore $a + b = 6$).
• Continue to make generalisations based on patterns in mathematics.	• Continue to make increasingly advanced generalisations based on patterns in mathematics.	• Continue to make increasingly advanced generalisations based on patterns in mathematics.
	• Make conjectures (statements) about mathematics and further develop the ability to convince others.	• Make conjectures (statements) about mathematics and further develop the ability to convince others.
	• Continue to make 'if … then …' statements.	• Continue to make 'if … then … ' statements, representing them using letters if able (e.g. if $2 + 4 = 6$, then $6 - 2 = 4$ represented using letters: if $a + b = c$ then $c - a = b$).

Always, sometimes, never

 # Key strategy

Give the children a statement and then ask whether it is it always, sometimes or never true.

Why it's effective

This line of questioning allows children to begin to develop the key skill of proving or disproving a statement, as well as introducing the concept of mathematical proof. This key strategy is very effective at encouraging children to make connections between different areas of mathematics.

Tips for use

This key strategy makes a particularly effective starter activity. It can also be effective when introducing a new focus or concept. It works particularly well if time is allowed for paired or grouped discussion, with children encouraged to discuss the statement together and come up with their answer (always, sometimes, never) and justification before feeding back to you or the class. You can play 'devil's advocate', giving children different examples to check against their decision. It can also work well to give children a statement about which they may have misconceptions.

The strategy can also be used as a powerful assessment tool by asking the same 'always, sometimes, never' question at the start and end of the unit. Through doing this you should be able to notice and evidence the increased sophistication in children's thinking and reasoning skills.

Children can also be given sets of statements to sort into 'always true', 'sometimes true' or 'never true'. These statements could be from one area of mathematics (e.g. all about fractions) or a mixture of areas. The activity can also be extended to ask how the statements can be changed to make them always true, sometimes true or never true.

Watch out

Children may ask what you need in order to say that something is always true.

This can be used as a really effective discussion point about the nature of mathematical proof. Ask: *How many examples do you need to give to prove a statement is not true? What do you need to do to prove a statement is always true?*

Try these

Below are some examples to introduce your class to this strategy. In these examples, the content level is sometimes lower than that set out in the National Curriculum for Year 2. This is to allow children to focus on the development of reasoning skills, without being restricted by subject knowledge.

Is it always, sometimes or never true that all multiples of 5 have a 5 in the ones place?
➤ *Let's write down some multiples of 5. What do we notice?*
➤ *Why is it that every other multiple of 5 ends in a 5?*

Is it always, sometimes or never true that the answer to a calculation follows the equals sign?
➤ *What about if we wrote a statement like 11 = ? + 3 or 22 = 14 + ?*
➤ *What does the equals sign actually mean?* (a balance)

 Case studies from the classroom

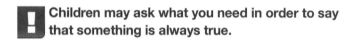 *A snippet from a conversation between two Year 2 children discussing the question: Is it always, sometimes or never true that a multiple of 5 ends in 5?*

Is it always, sometimes or never true that a number less than 10 + a number less than 10 = a number less than 10?

➤ *Let's write down some number sentences where this statement is true.*
➤ *Can we write down some statements where it is not true?*
➤ *Can we change the statement so that it would always be true? (E.g. a number less than 5 + a number less than 5 = a number less than 10)*

Is it always, sometimes or never true that taking away a 2-digit number from a 2-digit number always gives a 2-digit answer?

➤ *Let's write down some subtraction number sentences*
➤ *Can you think of an example where this isn't true?*
➤ *What do you notice about the examples where the statement isn't true?*

Is it always, sometimes or never true that adding three single-digit numbers above 4 gives you a 2-digit number?

➤ *Let's write down some number sentences involving three single-digit numbers above 4. What do you notice?*
➤ *What is the lowest answer you could make by adding three single-digit numbers above 4?*

Is it always, sometimes or never true that addition is commutative?

➤ *Let's write down some addition number sentences and then write down their reverse. Are the answers the same?*
➤ *Why is addition commutative?*
➤ *Can we say the same for subtraction?*

Is it always, sometimes or never true that you can make any coin value (e.g. 20p) by adding other coin values together (e.g. 10p + 10p)?

➤ *Let's write down all the coin values we know.*
➤ *Can we make them all by using other coin values?*

Is it always, sometimes, or never true that a 3-D shape has at least one vertex?

➤ *Can we name some 3-D shapes that do not have any vertices?*

Is it always, sometimes or never true that a hexagon has equal sides?

➤ *Is it always, sometimes or never true that a hexagon has equal sides?*
➤ *Can you draw a hexagon that doesn't have equal sides?*

Is it always, sometimes or never true that a picture on a pictogram represents one piece of data?

➤ *Does this always have to be the case?*

Activities and investigations

14 Total patterns
15 The fraction family

Child A: Well, 5, 15, 25 are all in the 5 times table.

Child B: But there are some numbers that don't end in 5, like 10 and 20.

Child A: I think it's sometimes, and that multiples of 5 either end in 5 or 0.

Key strategy

Give the children a statement and ask them to give you examples that meet the statement. Then ask for another example and another … .

Why it's effective

This strategy encourages children to give specific examples which meet a given general statement. By asking them to repeatedly give another example that meets the statement, children develop their skills of specialising, that is the skill of giving specific examples. This strategy also provides a good opportunity to assess children's developing understanding of an area of mathematics.

Tips for use

Initially ask children for one example that meets the criteria set, and then, after a pause, ask for another. Continue doing this, pausing slightly each time to allow children to think about and construct their response, until children have exhausted the possible responses and/or a generalisation has been made.

You can focus the use of this strategy by introducing caveats, e.g. *Give me another that involves a number greater than 100.*

This strategy can be used in conjunction with other key strategies in this book, including 'If this is the answer, what's the question?' and 'Strange and obvious'.

It is useful to analyse children's methods for creating their responses. Do they have a structured approach to generating further responses, are they using a generalisations, or do their answers appear to be given at random?

Encourage children to make generalisations by focusing on what their responses have in common. After generating responses independently, children could be encouraged to discuss their responses and draw out what they have in common.

The activity can be extended further by asking children how many possible answers there are, asking them to convince you that their response is true. This is especially interesting if there is an infinite number of responses, as the reason for this can be explored. Mathematical thinking can also be developed further by asking children to convince you of the lowest and highest possible answers.

Watch out

Children sticking to one rule/generalisation where there are other possible options.

Whilst the generating of generalisations can be a valuable outcome from using this strategy, sometimes this will not be the intended outcome and children will become 'fixed' on a certain rule or generalisation to generate each response. In these instances simply modifying the statement by introducing a caveat, as described above, is an effective way to focus children's thinking.

Try these

Below are some examples to introduce your class to this strategy. In these examples, the content level is sometimes lower than that set out in the National Curriculum for Year 2. This is to allow children to focus on the development of reasoning skills, without being restricted by subject knowledge.

Case studies from the classroom

A snippet from a conversation between a Year 2 child and a teacher discussing ways to show 15.

Can you give me an example of a multiple of 2? Another, another, another … .

➤ *What do your responses have in common?*
➤ *What if you answer had to be greater than 20?*
➤ *What if it your answer had to be a three-digit number?*

Can you give me a way of making 20p with coins? Another, another, another … .

➤ *What if you had to use at least/exactly four coins?*
➤ *What if you had to only use coins worth less than 5p?*
➤ *How do you know you have found all the possible answers?*

Can you give me an example of a shape with two sides of equal length? Another, another, another … .

➤ *Is there any shape you couldn't make with two equal sides?*
➤ *What if it had to be a quadrilateral?*
➤ *What if it had to be a quadrilateral that wasn't an oblong?*
➤ *What if it had to be a hexagon?*

Can you give me an example of two numbers that add together to give a total higher than 50? Another, another, another … .

➤ *What if one of the numbers had to be below 50?*
➤ *What if both numbers had to be below 50?*
➤ *What if one number had to be below 25?*

Can you give me a way of partitioning the number 84? Another, another, another … .

➤ *What if it had to be partitioned non-canonically? (i.e. not down the tens and units boundaries)*
➤ *What if it had to be partitioned into three numbers?*
➤ *What if one of the numbers had to be 14?*

Can you give me an example of numbers with a difference of 4? Another, another, another … .

➤ *What if one of the numbers had to be 3? 8?*
➤ *What if one of the numbers had to be above 100?*

Can you show me a way to represent the multiplication 3 × 5 = 15? Another, another, another … .

➤ *What if you had to use counters?*
➤ *What If you had to display it in an array? Is there more than one array that you could make?*
➤ *What if you had to represent it on a number line?*

Can you give me an example of a 3-D shape? Another, another, another … .

➤ *What if it couldn't be a cube?*
➤ *What if it had to have one curved face?*
➤ *What if it had to have an odd number of vertices?*
➤ *What if all its faces had to be quadrilaterals?*

Can you give me an example of a pattern made out of three different shapes? Another, another, another … .

➤ *What if the section of the pattern that repeated has more than three different shapes in?*
➤ *What if the section of the pattern that repeated has more than six different shapes in?*
➤ *What if you could use different shapes and colours?*

Can you give me an example of a question you could ask children in our class to find out some information? Another, another, another … .

➤ *What if it had to have only two possible answers?*
➤ *What if each child could give more than one answer?*

 Activities and investigations

1 Matchstick challenge
2 Many, many methods
3 The story of 20
5 Calculation families
6 Put it in the right place
13 Lunchtime fun
17 Fruit bowl challenge

Teacher: Is there any other way we could show 15? How about in groups?

Child A: Put 15 counters in a line.

Child A: Show an array of 3 × 5 counters.

3 **Convince me**

 ## Key strategy

Make a statement to the children and ask them to decide whether it is accurate or not, then explain their reasoning to convince you.

Why it's effective

This key strategy encourages children to look at the structure of mathematics and is another way for children to explore the concept of mathematical proof. Through trying to convince someone that a statement is true, children will begin to make generalisations and develop their thinking.

Tips for use

This strategy is particularly effective when the statements given to children are statements which they 'take for granted' and assume are correct. Asking children to convince you that these are true (e.g. *multiplication is the opposite of division, i.e. 3 × 4 = 12, 12 ÷ 4 = 3*) will deepen their conceptual understanding of mathematics.

Whilst the strategy can be effectively used with given statements, perhaps the most powerful use of this strategy is in response to children's own statements and can sometimes lead to an impromptu, but valuable, diversion from the planned activity.

The strategy can be used alongside the 'Always, sometimes, never' strategy to help develop and prompt children's thinking.

When supporting children in responding to this strategy, the following 'USE ME' stages are often useful (see page 10 for more detail):

- **Understanding:** do children understand the statement?
- **Specialising:** looking at one, or a small number of examples of the statement.
- **Encouraging representations:** *how could we represent the statement, or our specific examples of the statement?*
- **Making generalisations:** *by looking at our specialised examples, can we begin to make a statement that applies to all examples?*
- **Extending:** provide a further, linked, question for children to explore. This often works well when used with other strategies from this book.

Watch out

! **Children may respond with 'Because it is ... .'**

When children are first asked to convince someone that a statement is true, they often respond with a response along the lines of 'Because it is ... .' or 'Because my teachers have always told me.' Children can be encouraged to respond in the form 'It is true that ... because ... .'

! **Children may not know where to start.**

First check if children have the required prior knowledge and understanding to be able to convince you that the statement is true. If they do, then providing some initial probing questions, perhaps by using 'panic envelopes' (see Problem solving techniques on page 11), can help them to follow a line of reasoning

Try these

Below are some examples to introduce your class to this strategy. In these examples, the content level is sometimes lower than that set out in the National Curriculum for Year 2. This is to allow children to

 Case studies from the classroom

A snippet from a conversation between two Year 2 children discussing the question: Convince me me that 60>40.

focus on the development of reasoning skills, without being restricted by subject knowledge.

Convince me ... that addition is the opposite of subtraction.
➤ (Understanding) *What does addition and subtraction mean?*
➤ (Specialising) *Let's look at an example. How about 13 + 12 = 25. What is the opposite of this statement?*
➤ (Encouraging representations) *How could we represent an addition? How about a subtraction?*
➤ (Making generalisations) *Is this the same for all addition and subtraction facts?*
➤ (Extending) *Are there any other operations that are the opposite of each other?*

Convince me ... that multiplication and addition are linked.
➤ (Understanding and Making generalisations) *What does multiplication mean? What do we mean when we say multiply a number?*
➤ (Specialising) *Can you come up with a multiplication number sentence?*
➤ (Making generalisations) *How are these multiplications and additions linked?*
➤ (Extending) *Are there any other operations that are linked to each other in some way?*

Convince me ... that all of these shapes are quadrilaterals.

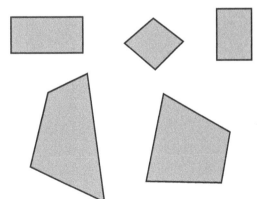

➤ (Understanding and Making generalisations) *What is a quadrilateral? How can we define a quadrilateral? (A quadrilateral is any shape with four straight sides.*
➤ (Specialising) *Can you come up with a multiplication number sentence?*
➤ *So, do all of these shapes meet the definition of a quadrilateral?*
➤ *Are squares and rectangles also quadrilaterals?*
➤ (Extending) *Could you draw me a really strange quadrilateral?*

Convince me ... that all of these shapes are quadrilaterals.
➤ *What does the < sign mean?*
➤ *Is this the case here? Is 20 smaller than 90? How do we know?*

 Activities and investigations

2   Many, many methods
4   Double your robot
5   Calculation families
6   Put it in the right place
7   Moneybox puzzle
9   A difference of 5
10 Coin totals

Child A: I think > means bigger than.

Child A: Yes, and that's true as we know 60 has 2 more tens than 40.

Child B: Yes, and that's true as we know 60 has 2 more tens than 40.

Key strategy

Ask the children to give you an example of a 'hard' and 'easy' answer to a question, explaining why one is 'hard' and the other 'easy'.

Why it's effective

This strategy encourages children to think closely about the structure of mathematics and enables them to demonstrate a conceptual understanding of concepts. Children enjoy the challenge of coming up with 'hard' examples that still meet the requirements set out in the question.

The choices children make when responding to this strategy often provide valuable information about what they find difficult, which may not always be what you expect!

Tips for use

Unlike most of the strategies in this book, this strategy generally works best if children are encouraged to respond individually first. Once they have come up with their own 'hard' and 'easy' responses they should then be encouraged to discuss and compare these with a partner or larger group. The strategy 'What's the same? What's different?' can be used here to encourage children to compare and contrast their responses and draw out key themes/concepts.

Children should be encouraged to explain why the examples they have given are 'hard' or 'easy'.

This could be by way of a written explanation or by convincing their partner/an adult verbally that their responses are 'hard' or 'easy'.

Watch out

Children responding to the request for a 'hard' example of a number with three tens by giving a number from 36 to 39.

Children are likely to stick to 30 or low 30s numbers and to consider the higher 30s numbers as harder. Ask the children to convince you why this is a hard example, and then discuss how this could be made harder, e.g. a 3-digit number with three tens such as 137.

Try these

Below are some examples to introduce your class to this strategy. In these examples, the content level is sometimes lower than that set out in the National Curriculum for Year 2. This is to allow children to focus on the development of reasoning skills, without being restricted by subject knowledge.

Give me a hard and easy example of an addition number sentence with the answer 60.
➤ *Easy: 130 + 30 as it is based on a known doubles fact*
➤ *Hard: 23 + 37 as the numbers are both above 20; 11 + 33 + 16 as it has more than two numbers*

Give me a hard and easy example of a pair of numbers which total 100.
➤ *Easy: 60 + 40 as it is based on my number bonds to 10*
➤ *Hard: 32 + 68 as it isn't based on my number bonds to 10 and isn't close to a known double*

 Case studies from the classroom

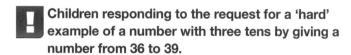 *A snippet from a conversation between two Year 2 children discussing the question: Give me a hard and easy example of an addition number sentence.*

Give me a hard and easy example of a number in the 5 times table.

➤ Easy: 5 as it's the first number in the two times table
➤ Hard: 85 as it's above 12 × 5

Give me a hard and easy example of a number to find 1 more than.

➤ Easy: 6 as it is a single-digit number
➤ Hard: 89 as it involves crossing the tens boundary; 809 as it is a 3-digit number with zero in the tens place

Give me a hard and easy example of an addition number sentence

➤ Easy: 2 + 1 = as it involves two low value numbers and is a known fact
➤ Hard: 49 + 58 as the answer would cross the tens and hundreds boundary, and require writing 107 rather than 1007 (one hundred, and seven)

Give me a hard and easy example of a subtraction number sentence.

➤ Easy: 5 – 3 as it involves two low value numbers with a small difference
➤ Hard: 37 – ? = 12 as it involves a missing number and is not set out in the 'usual' format; 132 – 86 as it crosses the hundreds and tens boundaries

Give me a hard and easy example way to partition 38.

➤ Easy: 30 and 8 as it is partitioned along the tens and units boundary (canonically); 15 + 15 + 8 as it uses a known doubles fact
➤ Hard: 2 + 15 +10 + 5 + 6 as it is partitioned into five numbers, none of which are 'obvious' within 38

Give me a hard and easy pair of numbers to compare using the < or > signs.

➤ Easy: 2 and 60 as there is a clear difference between the numbers and one is a 2-digit number whilst the other is a single-digit number
➤ Hard: 89 and 98 as they contain the same digits and are both 2-digit numbers

Give me a hard and easy number to find half of.

➤ Easy: 8 as it is based on a simple known doubles fact (4 + 4)
➤ Hard: 78 as it is a 2-digit number; 7 as it does not give a whole number answer

Give me an easy and hard way to measure the width of this piece of paper.

➤ Easy: using rulers in centimetres as this is a standard unit and one 30 cm ruler will fit across the width of the paper
➤ Hard: using counting bears as this is a non-standard unit and we'd also need a lot of them

Make me an easy and hard pictogram.

➤ Easy: a pictogram where each item represents one of something
➤ Hard: a pictogram where each item represents more than one of something

 Activities and investigations

9   A difference of 5

Child A: 20 + 20 is easy because you can use double 2 to help you.

Child B: 46 + 37 is harder because the ones are bigger and it is harder to work out the total of the ones.

Key strategy

Give the children an answer and ask them to come up with as many questions as possible that could have that answer.

Why it's effective

This strategy encourages children to think creatively and explore the structure of the numbers and mathematics. Children will begin to spot and use patterns and through this make their own generalisations.

Tips for use

Children should be encouraged to share their possible questions in pairs and collate them together, explaining their possible questions to their partner if needed. Finally, each pair could be invited to share a possible question with the class, picking a question which they think no one else will have come up with. This provides a great opportunity for further questioning, which could incorporate some of the other key strategies, such as 'Convince me ...', 'Always, sometimes, never', and 'Another, another, another'.

Recording possible questions on a mind map, with the answer in the middle is an effective way to record responses to this key strategy. On-line collective canvases such as lino-it (www.linoit.com) and padlet (www.padlet.com) can also be effective to collaboratively record possible answers.

Children can also be encouraged to put their possible questions into categories. Some obvious categories could be questions related to multiplication, questions which involve an odd number, questions which are in context, etc. However, asking children to categorise their possible questions themselves is often surprising and creates a good opportunity for further discussion.

The strategy can also be easily differentiated by adding set criteria to challenge or support children, e.g. only questions that involve even numbers, only questions that involve multiplication, etc.

The strategy also provides a great opportunity to encourage children to follow patterns. For example, if a suggested question is $23 + 36 = 59$ can they also see that $32 + 26 = 59$ could be another question?

Finally the strategy can also work well if it is run as a timed competition. Set a time limit and challenge children to come up with as many possible questions as they can, before then going through some of the follow-up stages suggested above.

Finally the strategy can also work well if it is run as a timed competition. Set a time limit and challenge children to come up with as many possible questions as they can, before then going through some of the follow-up stages suggested above.

Watch out

 Children may get stuck with one rule.

Sometimes children will get stuck with one 'rule' or type of question, e.g. addition questions. This can easily be overcome by asking the child to make their next question different: *What about a question involving a fraction? Give me a question involving numbers over 100.*

Case studies from the classroom

A snippet from a conversation between two Year 2 children discussing what the question could be if the answer was 20.

Try these

Below are some examples to introduce your class to this strategy. In these examples, the content level is sometimes lower than that set out in the National Curriculum for Year 2. This is to allow children to focus on the development of reasoning skills, without being restricted by subject knowledge.

If the answer is 5, what could the possible questions be?
➤ *Challenge: Your question must include division.*

If the answer is 40, what could the possible questions be?
➤ *Challenge: Your question must include multiplication.*

If the answer is 2, what could the possible questions be?
➤ *Challenge: Your question must include a fraction of a number.*

If the answer is the ones digit is always even, what could the possible questions be?
➤ *Challenge: One of your questions must refer to properties of numbers.*

If the answer is less than 20, what could the possible questions be?
➤ *Challenge: Your question must include an operation.*

If the answer is 8 girls what could the possible questions be?
➤ *Challenge: Your question must involve addition.*

If the answer is 6 what could the possible questions be?
➤ *Challenge: Your question must refer to 2-D shapes.*

If the answer is a triangle, what could the possible questions be?
➤ *Challenge: Your question must refer to 3-D shapes.*

If the answer is 100 cm, what could the possible questions be?
➤ *Challenge: Your question must refer to another unit of measure.*

If the answer is 5, 10, 15, 20 what could the possible questions be?
➤ *Challenge: Your questions must refer to a multiplication table.*

Activities and investigations

3   The story of 20

Child A: Well, we could have 18 + 2.

Child B: Yes, but that's a bit boring.

Child A: How about a word problem? Like there were 17 pirates on a ship and 3 more came aboard, how many are there altogether?

6 Maths stories

Key strategy

Give the children a number, geometry concept or measure and ask them to write its 'story', that is as much as they know or can work out about it.

Why it's effective

This strategy encourages children to explore everything they know about a mathematical concept and is therefore particularly effective at developing children's subject knowledge whilst also encouraging them to reason.

Through telling a 'story', children are also likely to form and use their own generalisations and patterns, which can be a great starting point for further discussion.

Tips for use

Start by giving the children a number a geometry concept, (e.g. a shape) or a measure. Then ask children to write as many statements as they can about the item given.

For example, when given a number children may choose to look at the classification of the number (odd, even etc.), the multiplication tables the number is in, doubling and halving the number, sums and differences that lead to the number, number bonds related to the number etc.

As children create their 'story' they are likely to begin to create and use their own generalisations and patterns. Discussing these with children using the 'What else do we know?' and 'What do we notice?' key strategies is particularly effective.

This strategy can also work well as an individual or paired activity, followed by a class 'race' to record as many different elements of the numbers 'story' on a interactive whiteboard within a given time limit.

Watch out

! Children may focus on one pattern.

Children often get 'locked on' to one pattern, e.g. *doubling and halving, or following addition/ subtraction sequences.* Encourage children to explore other patterns by setting a target number of 'unrelated' facts that they record.

! Children may 'run out' of facts to record.

Sometimes children will appear to run out of facts to record. Draw children's attention to patterns within what they have recorded so far and ask: *What else do we know?* A bank of prompt questions may also be useful, providing prompts for things to investigate, e.g. *What number is double the number? What are the factors of the number?*

Try these

Below are some examples to introduce your class to this strategy. In these examples, the content level is sometimes lower than that set out in the National Curriculum for Year 2. This is to allow children to focus on the development of reasoning skills, without being restricted by subject knowledge.

Case studies from the classroom

A snippet from a conversation between two Year 2 children exploring the story of 11.

General prompt questions to use with number-based stories (including fractions).
➤ *Is the number odd or even?*
➤ *Which times tables that you know is this number in?*
➤ *What is double the number? Double this number?*
➤ *What is half the number? Half this number?*

➤ *What happens when you multiply the number by 10?*
➤ *What calculations could this number be involved in?*
➤ *Could this number be involved in any 'real-life' problems?*

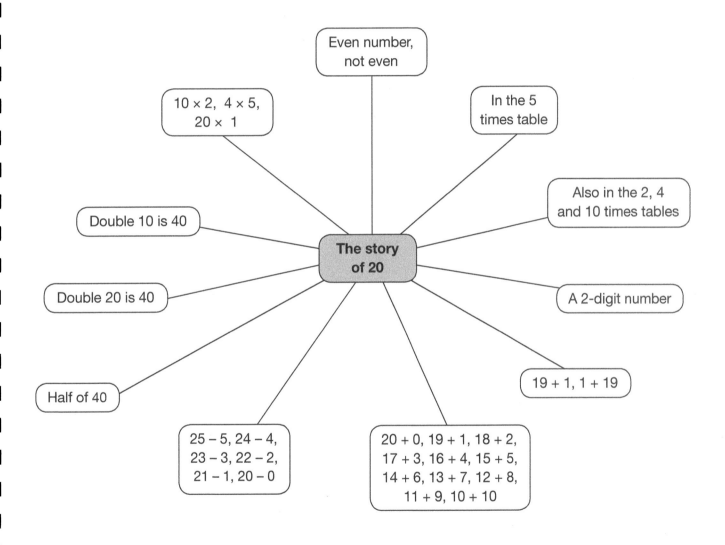

Even number, not even

10×2, 4×5, 20×1

In the 5 times table

Double 10 is 40

Also in the 2, 4 and 10 times tables

The story of 20

Double 20 is 40

A 2-digit number

Half of 40

$19 + 1$, $1 + 19$

$25 - 5$, $24 - 4$, $23 - 3$, $22 - 2$, $21 - 1$, $20 - 0$

$20 + 0$, $19 + 1$, $18 + 2$, $17 + 3$, $16 + 4$, $15 + 5$, $14 + 6$, $13 + 7$, $12 + 8$, $11 + 9$, $10 + 10$

Child A: We could add $5 + 5 + 2$ to make 12.

Child B: That's double 5 plus 2.

Child A: We could do $5 + 5 + 2 + 10 - 10$ because adding and taking away 10 are opposites so it doesn't change it.

7 Odd one out

Key strategy

Give the children a set of three or more numbers or statements and ask them to identify which number/statement is the odd one out and why.

Why it's effective

When children work to identify what is the odd one out, they will be conjecturing and reasoning about the items in the set. Almost without realising it, they will create their own generalisations, and test all parts of the set given to them against this to try and identify the 'odd one out'.

Tips for use

This strategy works particularly well when time for paired or grouped discussion is given, with children attempting to convince each other which item from the set is the odd one out.

To further increase the reasoning required, especially when children have had some experience responding to this strategy, always aim to choose the set of numbers/statements you provide so that there is more than one possible 'answer.' This can create a good debate in the classroom, with different children trying to convince each other that the number they have selected is the 'real' odd one out.

This strategy could also be combined with the 'Another, another, another' strategy, by asking children to generate further examples that would either be similar to the 'odd one out' or to the rest of the set.

Watch out

Children may not see the link between parts of the set.

Sometimes children will struggle to find the odd one out as they cannot spot the generalities (links) between different parts of the set. Focusing children's thinking using the 'What's the same? What's different?' key strategy, initially with pairs from the set, can help children see the similarities and differences between parts of the set. Using 'panic envelopes' (see page xx) containing key questions to focus thinking can also be effective in supporting children to see the link between parts of the set.

Try these

Below are some examples to introduce your class to this strategy. In these examples, the content level is sometimes lower than that set out in the National Curriculum for Year 2. This is to allow children to focus on the development of reasoning skills, without being restricted by subject knowledge.

Look at this set of numbers: 3, 6, 9, 11. Which is the odd one out?
Possible 'odd one outs' with reasons and key questions/follow-ups:
➤ *6: the only even number*
➤ *11: the only number that you would not say if you counted in 3s from 0*
  Which times tables are some of these numbers in?

Addition, subtraction, multiplication. Which is the odd one out?
Possible 'odd one outs' with reasons:
➤ *Subtraction: you normally end up with less than you started with*
➤ *Subtraction: it's not commutative, but addition and multiplication are*

Case studies from the classroom

A snippet from a conversation between three Year 2 children discussing the question: Look at this set of numbers: 23, 16, 3. Which is the odd one out?

➤ *Multiplication: addition and subtraction can be thought to be opposite to each other*

➤ *Subtraction: it normally doesn't involve addition. You can think of multiplication as adding the same number over and over again (repeated addition).*

£2, 2p, 50p, 20p, 10p, 70p: which is the odd one out?

Possible 'odd one outs' with reasons:

➤ *£2: the only one worth more than 50p*

➤ *£2: the biggest coin (in size)*

➤ *70p: the only value that can't be made with just one coin*

➤ *50p: the only value that cannot be made with two coins*

➤ *2p: the lowest value in the list*

➤ *2p: it can't be made by combining any other of the values in the list*

Look at these fractions: $\frac{1}{3}$, $\frac{1}{4}$, $\frac{3}{4}$. Which is the odd one out?

Possible 'odd one outs' with reasons and key questions/follow-ups:

➤ *$\frac{1}{3}$: only fraction with a numerator (top number) greater than 1*

➤ *$\frac{1}{3}$: only fraction that is in thirds*

What does a fraction represent? (a proportion)

Activities and investigations

Child A: 23 is the odd one out because it is the only 2-digit number.

Child B: 16 is the odd one out because it is even.

Child C: 3 because it has 1-digit.

8 Strange and obvious

Key strategy

Ask the children to give a strange and obvious example of a statement. For some statements children will also be able to begin to develop a general example of the statement.

Why it's effective

This key strategy encourages children to think about the structure of mathematics and the definition of the statements given. Through focusing on what makes a strange or obvious example of a given statement children have to think carefully about the statement given, the criteria needed to meet the statement, and what examples they could give. The encouragement to give a strange example encourages children to push the boundaries of their understanding, whilst if they are able and it is appropriate to the statement given, the general example encourages children to begin to develop their ability to generalise.

Tips for use

This key strategy could be used either as part of shared learning, as the main activity in the lesson or as an effective plenary. Children should be encouraged to explain their choices, either verbally or in writing, which will encourage them to think about the definition of the given statement and the general structure of mathematics. The strategy works particularly well if children are encouraged to discuss and convince each other that their examples

fit with the statement and are strange, obvious or general. When working in pairs, children can also be encouraged to think of reasons why their partner's responses may not be strange, obvious (or general).

Encourage children first to state record an **obvious** example. *What is the first example you think of? Why is this the first example that you think of?* They can always replace their obvious example with a 'more obvious' example whilst they are thinking through the activity.

Then ask children to think of their **strange** example. Encourage them to think about the definition and criteria of the statement given. *What fits what we know about the statement, but isn't obvious?*

Finally, for some statements, children should be encouraged to think about a **general** example. This will deepen their thinking about the statement given.

Watch out

! **The rush for a really big or small number.**

In numerical questions, children will often state a really large or small strange number. Discuss with the children if, just because an example is really large or small, it is strange. *What makes it strange? Is it really quite obvious?* You can also modify the question to remove the temptation to go really large, e.g. *Can you give me a strange example of an odd number that is below 20?*

! **Children's general statements not being general.**

Using the strategy 'Always, sometimes, never' to encourage children to check their general statements can help children ensure their statements are truly general.

Case studies from the classroom

A snippet from a conversation between two Year 2 children discussing strange and obvious odd numbers.

Try these

The examples below were given by children who trialled this resource. Example follow-up questions are provided where appropriate.

Give me a strange, obvious and general example of an odd number over 100.
➤ *Strange: 1003 Why is 1003 peculiar? How do you now it's odd?*
➤ *Obvious: 103 Why is 103 obvious? Is it the first odd number after 100?*
➤ *General: A number which has three or more digits and ends in the digits 1, 3, 5, 7, 9.*

Give me a strange, obvious and general example of a multiple of 3
➤ *Strange: : 42, as it's above 12 lots of 3*
➤ *Obvious: 3, as it's the first multiple of 3.*
➤ *General: Any number that can be divided by 3 exactly.*

Give me a strange, obvious and general example of two numbers which, when subtracted, give the answer 24.

Give me a strange, obvious and general example of a fraction of a number.

Give me a strange, obvious and general example of a cuboid.

Give me a strange, obvious and general example of a repeating pattern.

Activities and investigations

11 Polyhedron Primary

Child A: 1 is obvious because it's the first odd number.

Child B: For strange we can have ⁻1 because it's a negative number.

Child A: If we do general, all odd numbers end in 1, 3, 5, 7 or 9.

9 Silly answers

Key strategy

Ask the children to give you a 'silly' answer to a question and explain why it is a silly answer.

Why it's effective

By asking children to give you a 'silly' answer to a question they will have to reason about the range which the possible 'correct' answers could fall into. This will require them to consider the properties that the question entails, and will involve them in making a generalisation about the 'correct' answer(s) in order to explain why their answer is silly.

Tips for use

Always ensure you ask children to justify their silly answer and explain why it can't possibly be a 'correct' answer.

Children can also be asked to create a number of 'silly' answers and then to order them in order of 'silliness'. Encourage them to identify which 'silly' answer is close to the 'real' answer or involves a common error/misconception. This can be a great way to address misconceptions with children.

Modifiers can also be added to the base question to restrict the range of possible silly answers. Depending on the restrictions added, this can prompt deeper thinking and reasoning.

This strategy works well when children are given the opportunity to discuss their 'silly' answer(s) and reasons why they are 'silly'. The strategy 'What's the same? What's different?' can be used to encourage children to compare, contrast and look for links between their 'silly' answers.

Watch out

 Children may always give very large answers.

Children's natural instinct when asked for a 'silly' answer often is to go for a very large answer, e.g. *4 billion trillion, infinity,* etc. Depending on the question given, either ask children if they can prove that this is not an answer to the question or place a restriction on the range of answers allowed.

Try these

Below are some examples to introduce your class to this strategy. In these examples, the content level is sometimes lower than that set out in the National Curriculum for Year 2. This is to allow children to focus on the development of reasoning skills, without being restricted by subject knowledge.

Give me a silly answer for a way of partitioning 23.
Prompt questions:
➤ *What does partitioning mean?*

Example silly answers and justification:
➤ **23 + 1**: as it already includes 23, and when you partition you break the number down into numbers less than it
➤ **3 + 2**: *as this clearly won't give you any digits in the tens place of a number, and you need a 2 in the tens place for 23*

Give me a silly answer for 7 + ? = 20.
Prompt questions:
➤ *How would we work out the missing number?*

Example silly answers and justification:
➤ **10**: *as that would be 15, as it's simple to take 10 away from a number*
➤ **28**: *as it's higher than 25, so can't equal 12 when you take it away from 25*

Case studies from the classroom

A snippet from a conversation between two Year 2 children discussing the silly answers for a way to partition 23.

➤ **14**: *as the last digit is not 3. We know it must be, as the difference between the last digits in the two numbers we know is 3.*

Give me a silly answer for a number sentence that is linked to 4 × 5 = 20.
Prompt question:
➤ *What number sentences would be linked? How else could we rewrite this number sentence? (explore commutatively)*

Example silly answers and justification:
➤ **4 + 5 = 9**: *as this clearly does not involve anything to do with the multiplication statement given*

Give me a silly answer for a unit to measure the side of this book.
Prompt questions:
➤ *What are we measuring?*
➤ *What would you estimate the length of the side of the book to be?*

Example silly answers and justification:
➤ **200 g:** *as g is a measure for mass, not length*
➤ **2 mm:** *as 2 mm is less than 1 cm, and this is clearly more than 1 cm long*
➤ **200 cm:** *as this is more than 1 m, and the book is not 1 m long*

Give me a silly answer for a drawing of a square
Example silly answers and justification:
➤ Because it has more than four sides

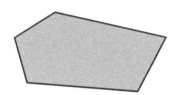

➤ Because it has more than four sides

➤ Because quadrilaterals are polygons and therefore all their sides need to be straight

Give me a silly answer for $\frac{1}{3}$ of 12.
Prompt questions:
➤ *Will $\frac{1}{3}$ of 12 be bigger or smaller than 12?*

Example silly answers and justification:
➤ **6**: *as 6 is half of 12, not a 1/3*
➤ **18**: *as 18 is above 12, and 1/3 is a way of showing a proportion (part of) 12*

Give me a silly answer for the question if the answer is 86.

Example silly answers and justification:
➤ **86 – 11**: *as you are taking away a positive number from your target answer, which will always result in a smaller number*
➤ **8 × 10**: *as you are multiplying by 10, so you are making your starting number 10 times bigger, which would be 80, not 86*

Activities and investigations

5   Calculation families
7   Moneybox puzzle
9   A difference of 5

Child A: Well, 2 + 3 would be silly, as it equals 5 and has no tens.

Child B: 30 + 30 would be silly, as 30 is over 23 so can't be part of 23 when it is partitioned.

10 What do you notice?

 Key strategy

Ask the children 'What do you notice?' about a number, set of numbers, shape or mathematical statement.

Why it's effective

This strategy encourages children to look deeper at the structure of mathematics. Through answering the question 'What do you notice?' children will be making their own generalisations and testing them against specific examples.

Tips for use

This strategy is very effective when children are given time to talk and discuss the statement with a partner or small groups, before feeding back to the class (or larger group) with the expectation that they convince the larger group of what they notice.

When using this strategy, you can provide children with sets of numbers/mathematical objects (e.g. *2, 4, 6, 8, 10; a rectangle, a square and triangle*) or general statements/properties (e.g. *all numbers in the 2 times table*).

Children's reasoning skills can be further developed by asking follow-up questions or providing follow-up statements once children have responded to the initial 'What do you notice?' question. The strategy 'Always, sometimes, never' true often works well as a follow-up to a 'What do you notice?' question as this allows children to further develop their generalisations.

This strategy can also be used alongside many of the other key strategies, which can help to focus children's thinking and reasoning.

Watch out

Children may not see the general statements.

Sometimes children will be unable to independently state the generality or generalities relating to the statement which has been given. To help children see the generality, use follow-up questions, which could involve some of the other key strategies. 'What's the same? What's different?' is particularly effective here. Panic envelopes, with follow-up questions (see page 11) can also be used.

Try these

Below are some examples to introduce your class to this strategy. In these examples, the content level is sometimes lower than that set out in the National Curriculum for Year 2. This is to allow children to focus on the development of reasoning skills, without being restricted by subject knowledge.

What do you notice about the numbers you say when you count in 5s from 0?
➤ *Can you list some of the numbers you would say?*
➤ *What's the same? What's different about these numbers?*
➤ (For more able children only) *Can you think why this happens?*

What do you notice about this set of numbers: 3, 6, 9, 12 … ?
➤ *What would the next number be in this sequence?*
➤ *What would the 10th number in this sequence be?*

Case studies from the classroom

A snippet from a conversation between two Year 2 children discussing what they noticed about a square.

What do you notice about a square?
➤ *How many sides does a square have?*
➤ *What is special about these sides?*

What do you notice about this pattern?

➤ *What do you notice about the direction the shapes are pointing?*
➤ *How have they been moved from one shape to the next in our pattern?*
➤ *How much have they been turned by?*
➤ *What will be next shape in this pattern?*

Activities and investigations

Child A: Well, it has four sides.

Child B: Yes! And they are all the same length, so it's got four equal length sides.

What else do we know?

 Key strategy

Give the children an 'If ... ' statement, e.g. 2 × 5 is 10, and ask them what else they know based on this statement.

Why it's effective

This strategy encourages children to see the links that exist in all areas of mathematics. It encourages them to reason and combine other known facts with the statement. This activity works particularly well as a starter or plenary, or as an early morning challenge.

Tips for use

Provide the statement and allow children to record everything else they know. Adding a time and/or quantity challenge (e.g. *Can you state at least five other facts in two minutes?*) can help to add an element of competition!

Try asking the whole class to work on a statement individually, then to share their related facts with a partner, then ask each pair to share with the class a related fact that they think that no one else would have come up with. This approach pushes children to think deeper and go beyond the 'obvious' related facts. A mind map can be a useful tool for recording responses to this strategy, with children recording groups of related facts on each arm of their mind maps.

You can also work with children on the 'automatic' related facts that they should be able to state almost instantaneously, e.g. commutative facts, (e.g. *7 × 8 = 8 × 7*).

The 'Strange and obvious' strategy can also be used alongside 'What else do we know?' to deepen the thinking from this strategy.

Watch out

! **Children may 'stall'.**

Sometimes children will come up with a few 'obvious' related facts (perhaps using inverses, etc.), but then struggle to see any other related facts. Asking children to discuss ideas together can help overcome this.

! **Facts/statements may not be related.**

Sometimes children will provide facts/statements that appear to have no clear relation to the given statement, but be careful not to say categorically that it is not a related fact. Instead, encourage them to explain how it is related, talking you, or another child through the steps they have taken to form this related fact. Analysing untrue 'facts' given by children can also help expose any misconceptions that they may hold.

Try these

Below are some examples to introduce your class to this strategy. In these examples, the content level is sometimes lower than that set out in the National Curriculum for Year 2. This is to allow children to focus on the development of reasoning skills, without being restricted by subject knowledge.

Case studies from the classroom

A snippet from a conversation between three Year 2 children discussing what else they know if they know 5 × 3 = 15.

If we know that 5 × 6 = 30, what else do we know?

➤ *What is special about multiplication? Can we rewrite this number sentence in any other way and keep the sentence true? (6 × 5 = 30)*

➤ *Is there a subtraction number sentence linked to this addition sentence? (10 − 4 = 6, 10 − 6 = 4)*

➤ *5 + 5 + 5 + 5 + 5 + 5 = 30, 6 + 6 + 6 + 6 + 6 = 30*

➤ *30 ÷ 6 = 4, 30 ÷ 5 = 6*

➤ *50 × 6 = 300, 5 × 60 = 300, 50 × 60 = 3000*

If we know that $\frac{1}{2}$ of 6 = 3, what else do we know?

➤ *Is there another fraction that is equal to $\frac{1}{2}$? ($\frac{2}{4}$: $\frac{2}{4}$ of 6 = 3)*

➤ *Could we use this number sentence to help us work out half of 12?*

If we know that 32 + 32 = 64, what else do we know?

➤ *Can we double each number to make a related number sentence?*

➤ *Can we form a subtraction sentence using our knowledge of inverses?*

If we know that an odd number plus an odd number always equals an even number, what else do we know?

➤ *Can you give some examples of an odd number + odd number equalling an even number?*

➤ *Can we think about what happens to an odd number + even number?*

Activities and investigations

Child A: Multiplication can be done any way round, so we know that 3 x 5 = 15.

Child B: Aren't multiplication and division opposites? So could we say that 5 ÷ 3 = 15?

Child C: No, that's not right, but 15 ÷ 3 = 5.

Key strategy

Give the children at least two statements, objects or numbers and ask them to compare them by asking 'What's the same? What's different?'

Why it's effective

This strategy encourages children to compare and contrast. It fosters children's ability to spot patterns and similarities, to make generalisations and to spot connections between different aspects of mathematics. The open-ended nature of the key strategy enables all children to contribute, regardless of their ability and support can easily be added.

Tips for use

Introduce the two (or more) things that you want the children to compare and simply ask 'What's the same? What's different?' This can work well individually, or through paired or grouped discussion. You could ask children to write their ideas on sticky notes, and share these together as a class, discussing each statement as it is shared.

The strategy can be used with two things, but can also be effective when used with more, as this can help develop children's ability to spot relationships. The strategy can also be used effectively alongside the 'Odd one out' strategy.

Key prompt questions can also be provided to groups who may need more support, or more generally when you need to scaffold children's thinking in a particular direction. These could be provided on 'panic envelopes' (see Problem-solving techniques on page 11) which children should use only if they cannot think of anything that is the same/different themselves.

Watch out

Children may point out 'superficial' similarities/differences (e.g. *they are both numbers*).

These should not be discouraged and the more often children are exposed to this strategy, the more 'mathematical' their responses will become. Providing prompt questions or panic sheets as described above can help children focus their thinking and produce deeper similarities/differences, which demonstrates a greater level of reasoning.

Try these

Below are some examples to introduce your class to this strategy. In these examples, the content level is sometimes lower than that set out in the National Curriculum for Year 2. This is to allow children to focus on the development of reasoning skills, without being restricted by subject knowledge.

What's the same and what's different about 2 and 20?
➤ Same: both in the 2 times table, both have a digit sum (when you add up all the digits in the number) of 2, both contain the number 2.
➤ Different: 20 is a 2-digit number, 2 is a 1-digit number What's the same and what's different about … ?

 **Case studies from the classroom**

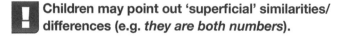 *A snippet from a conversation between two Year 2 children discussing what's the same and what's different about grams and kilograms.*

What's the same and what's different about addition and multiplication?

➤ Same: both often make numbers bigger, multiplication is repeated addition, both are operations.
➤ Different: multiplication is lots of the same number, where as addition is normally adding two or more different numbers together.

What's the same and what's different about 1/3 and 3/4?

➤ Same: both fractions, both a proportion
➤ Different: the numerator and denominators are not the same, they represent different proportions, the numerator in $\frac{3}{4}$ is bigger than 1.

What's the same and what's different between cm and m?

➤ Same: both ways of measuring a length
➤ Different: 1 m is much bigger than 1 cm

What's the same and what's different between a cube and a triangular based pyramid?

➤ Both 3-D shapes.
➤ They have different numbers of faces, edges and vertex.

What's the same and what's different about a pictogram and bar chart?

➤ Same: both show data, both are types of graphs
➤ Different: in a pictogram each block represents a set number of things. Bar graphs have axes with a scale on them which you have to read.
➤ Explore the different types of data possible to display on different types of graphs. graphs

Activities and investigations

2 Many, many methods
3 The story of 20
4 Double your robot
5 Calculation families
6 Put it in the right place
11 Polyhedron Primary
16 My robot friend
17 Fruit bowl challenge
18 Number square investigation

Child A: They are both ways of measuring weight.

Child B: A g is much smaller than a kg.

Child A: Yes, g is a 1000 times smaller.

13 Zooming in

Key strategy

Ask the children to give you an example that fits with a given criteria, (e.g. *an odd number*) and then 'zoom in' to give further criteria which their number has to fit (e.g. *an odd number which is also greater than 10*).

Why it's effective

This strategy encourages children to reason about mathematical properties and gets them re-evaluating the properties of their initial 'answer' to check it meets the additional criteria as it is revealed. Children will soon begin to try and anticipate how you may 'zoom in' to narrow down the criteria and make more reasoned choices for their initial 'answers'.

Tips for use

The key strategy is particularly effective when launching a new topic or focus area, as it can allow children to demonstrate their current knowledge, as well as encouraging them to explore the boundaries of their current understanding. The strategy is also particularly effective as a plenary or at the end of a topic in order to assess understanding.

The zooming in could be modelled using a game of 'guess who' with the whole class, e.g. *All stand. Stay standing if you have one or more brothers. So people with brothers are standing, people without brothers are sitting. Keep standing if you have a cat. Who is standing? People with brothers and cats. Who is sitting? People without brothers, but they could have a cat.*

Children should normally be allowed to change their answer if it does not fit the new criteria revealed, however you may want to reward children whose initial answer still met all criteria. You can, however, make the game competitive by saying that a child is 'out' if their number no longer fits. Keep revealing criteria until there is only one possible answer or there is only one child left. This encourages more sophisticated thinking as children try to anticipate what further criteria you will add to 'zoom in'.

Once you have revealed all of your criteria you can promote further reasoning and mathematical discussion by asking children if they can think of any other answers that would meet all of the 'zoomed in' criteria. This activity can also be combined with the 'Strange, obvious (general)' strategy. *Can you give a strange answer that would fit all the 'zoomed in' criteria?*

You can also use grids of numbers/images from which children select based on the criteria given. (An example grid is provided on the CD-ROM which you can adapt.) Depending on the content of your grid, this can either provide support for less able the children, or can provide extra challenge by restricting the possible choices when 'zooming in'.

Finally, children can also be asked to create their own set of 'Zooming in' criteria, which encourages them to think in more depth about properties of number/shape.

Watch out

Children may struggle to test their answers with further statements.

Ensure that children have a secure understanding of the terminology used in the statements given.

Case studies from the classroom

Teacher: Give me any number.

Child: 10

Child: 53

Teacher: That is greater than 50.

Working as pairs or in small groups on this activity can also help with this by providing a source of peer support. It may also be that the pace at which you are adding the further statements is too demanding for some children.

Try these

Below are some examples to introduce your class to this strategy. In these examples, the content level is sometimes lower than that set out in the National Curriculum for Year 2. This is to allow children to focus on the development of reasoning skills, without being restricted by subject knowledge.

Give me a number, any number.
➤ *Zoom in so the number is greater than 50.*
➤ *Zoom in so that the number is even.*
➤ *Zoom in so that the number would be said if you counted in 10s from 0.*

Give me a fraction.
➤ *Zoom in so that it shows quarters.*
➤ *Zoom in so that the fraction is less than 1.*
➤ *Zoom in so that the numerator (the top number of a fraction) is greater than 2.*
➤ *What fraction have you been left with?*

Draw me a polygon.
➤ *Zoom in so it is also a quadrilateral.*
➤ *Zoom in so that it has two sets of equal sides*

Give me a measure of length.
➤ *Zoom in so it is in centimetres.*
➤ *Zoom in so it is shorter than the length of this book.*

Give me/point to a number (This example could be completed using the grid provided on the CD-ROM)
➤ *Zoom in so that it is over 10.*

5	60	8	25
45	12	10	0
37	24	40	55
30	15	70	22
36	50	4	20

➤ *Zoom in so that it is under 40.*
➤ *Zoom in so that the number is in the 5 times table.*
➤ *Zoom in so that the number is also in the 2 times table.*
➤ *Zoom in so that the number is also in the 4 times table.*

Give me/point to a number in the 5 times table. (This example could be completed using the grid provided on the CD-ROM.)
➤ *Zoom in so the number is above 20.*
➤ *Zoom in so the number is above 50.*
➤ *Zoom in so the number is odd.*
➤ *Zoom in so the number is below 60.*

Only 55 fits all criteria. *Ask: If we zoomed out so the number didn't have to be under 60, would there be any other possible answers?*

Child: 58

Child: 52

Teacher: That is even.

Teacher: That would be said if you counted in tens from 8.

Key strategy

In addition to the key strategies outlined, the following question structures can also help embed problem solving and reasoning into day-to-day maths teaching.

Can you give me an example of ... ?
➤ *an odd number*
➤ *an operation that is commutative*
➤ *a number that you would say when you count in 5s from 0*
➤ *a polygon*
➤ *a fraction of a number*

What is the quickest or easiest way to ... ?
➤ *count in 5s from 0*
➤ *add in 5s from 0*
➤ *find out a fraction of a number*

What is/are ... an example of?
➤ *5, 10, 15* (numbers in the 5 times table)
➤ *triangle, square, irregular quadrilateral, pentagon* (polygons)
➤ $\frac{3}{4}$ (a fraction)

How can we be sure that ... ?
➤ *we have partitioned a number correctly*
➤ *triangles are polygons*
➤ *6 is half of 12*

Is ... a good explanation of ... ?
➤ *breaking a number into smaller numbers ... partitioning*
➤ *numbers that end in 2, 4 ,6, 8 ... even numbers*

What's the link between ... ?
➤ *3, 6, 9, 12*
➤ *addition and multiplication*
➤ $\frac{1}{4}, \frac{2}{4}, \frac{3}{4}$
➤ *cm, mm and m*

Activities and investigations

Learning objective
- To identify and describe the properties of 2-D shapes

Reasoning skills
- Identifying patterns
- Working systematically

Curriculum link
 Properties of shape: 2-D shapes

The problem

Problem 1

Matchstick challenge!

How many polygons do you know? Which ones can you make from a pile of matchsticks?

How many polygons can you make in ten minutes?

Your challenge

Find how many 2-D shapes you can make from different numbers of matchsticks.

Things to think about

- Did you know that polygon is the mathematical name for a 2-D shape?
- Can you visualise the shape you are making?
- Can you work systematically? Maybe you could start with different types of triangle?

Hint: **Start with regular shapes. Then try making sides of shapes that are two or three matchsticks long.**
There will be more than one shape that you can make from each number of matchsticks.

Year 2   *Problem Solving and Reasoning*

Background knowledge

- This problem asks children to make polygons from different numbers of matchsticks.
- A polygon is a straight sided two-dimensional shape. It has width and length, but no depth.
- Polygon comes from Greek. 'Poly-' means 'many' and '-gon' means 'angle'.
- Not all polygons are regular. A regular polygon is one whose sides and angles are all equal.
- With increasing numbers of matchsticks, children will be able to make a variety of irregular polygons.
- The children should be encouraged to work systematically, making all the possible triangles first, then quadrilaterals, then pentagons … .

- Challenging the children to make polygons that are not possible is a fantastic way to promote reasoning
- Polygons can include complex polygons that appear to be folded over themselves.
- The children could be taught about concave and convex polygons, i. e. the difference between a delta and a kite.
- Descriptions of polygons can be found at http://www.mathsisfun.com/geometry/polygons.html.

Launching the activity

> 1. Ask the children to visualise a 2-D shape.

> 2. Using 'think, pair, share,' allow the children to share the shapes that they visualised and describe them to the class. They should create a mental image first, then draw it as part of the 'pair' strategy. Sharing their ideas will naturally lead to further discussion about the properties of polygons.

> 3. Define a polygon and give the children an opportunity to share types of polygons that they know.

> 4. Share the poster with the children and ask: *How many 2-D polygons do you think you can make from different numbers of matchsticks?*

> 5. Give out the matchsticks (six to those less able, ten or more to more able children) without providing a demonstration. Explain that they should use all of the matchsticks they are given to make their shape. Children will find the challenge difficult, but it will promote reasoning.

> 6. Through a mini-plenary, give guidance as appropriate and set a time limit for the challenge. The children should be given enough time to have multiple opportunities for success and failure, thinking time and recording time. Highlight the strategies of 'another, another, another' and 'What's the same? What's different?' to focus children's thinking.

> 8. Bring the class back together and ask children to share their solutions.

Developing reasoning

> ➤ *Can you find a shape that can be made with this number of matchsticks?* **Another, another, another.**
> ➤ *Can you make a shape that no one else will make? Why do you think that no one else will make this shape?*
> ➤ *Compare three of the shapes that are made with the same number of matchsticks. Which one is the **odd one out**? Why?*
> ➤ *How many different pentagons (change as appropriate) can you make?* **What's the same? What's different?**

Providing differentiation

Support
By giving the children six matchsticks, they would be able to make an equilateral triangle, an oblong, a parallelogram, a delta and a kite.

Extension
Give the children more than ten or an odd number of matchsticks. The odd number will mean that familiar quadrilaterals will not be possible and the children will have to explore different possibilities, e.g. an irregular hexagon.

As an extra challenge, children could be challenged to making polyhedral (3-D shapes).

Key strategies

2 Another, another, another
7 Odd one out
12 What's the same? What's different?

Problem-solving approaches

Working systematically
Think pair share

Taking it further

Ask the children what shapes they can see around the classroom. Ask them if they could make the shapes out of classroom objects such as pencils, rulers etc.

2 Many, many methods

Learning objective	Reasoning skills	Curriculum link
• To apply knowledge of mental and written methods of calculation.	• Identifying patterns • Working systematically • Reasoning numerically	Number: addition and subtraction

The problem

> Problem 2
>
> ### Many, many methods
>
> You can do easy calculations and you can do hard calculations.
>
> You can do one calculation and you can do lots of calculations.
>
> But can you do the same calculation in lots of ways?
>
> **Things to think about**
>
> • Can you partition the numbers to make the calculation easier?
> • Can you draw the calculation in many different ways?
> • Can you calculate on a number line in different ways?
>
> **Your challenge**
>
> Use as many methods as you can think of to calculate 28 + 45 = ?
>
>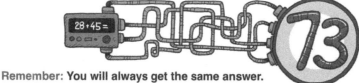
>
> Remember: **You will always get the same answer.**
> **Try to be imaginative by inventing ways of playing with the numbers 28 and 45 to find new routes to the answer.**
>
> RISING STARS Maths
>
> Year 2 — Problem Solving and Reasoning

Background knowledge

- Instead of relying on one or two methods of calculation, this problem challenges children to show how many ways they can calculate the fairly straightforward calculation 28 + 45.
- They could use drawings by drawing 28 circles in one pile, then 45 in another and count them all up.
- They could represent the numbers with interlocking cubes: 2 towers of 10 and a tower of 8 for 28, and 4 tens and 5 single cubes for 45. These can then be combined to bring the sets together.
- Calculations on a number line could start with either the 28 or the 45. Calculations could include:

  o adding the tens part of the number first, then adding the ones (units)
  o (from 28) counting up 2 (to get to the nearest 10) then adding 40 to make 70 and finally adding what is left to find the total. The same method could be used from 45.
  o using the compensation method by thinking of 28 as 30, or 45 as 50. First add on the multiple of 10, then take off what was previously added.

- Written methods could include:

  o writing the calculation down and saying, 'I did it in my head.'
  o partitioning the numbers: 20 + 8 + 40 + 5 = (20 + 40) + (8 + 5) = 60 + 13 = 73
  o using formal algorithms (column addition).

- This problem will naturally lead on to discussion about the most efficient methods for calculation and ways of representing calculations. An efficient method is one that works for that child and is one that they can do relatively quickly.

- Representation can be external and internal. Children need to experience a range of external representations to enable them to form their own internal ones. The more models and images they internalise, the better they will be at calculating.

Launching the activity

1. Write a range of number sentences and representations of calculations on the board that all use addition and all equal the same number.

2. Ask: *What do you notice?* and *What's the same? What's different?* about the calculations.

3. Elicit that they all equal the same number and that they are all different ways of calculating using the same numbers.

4. Share the poster with the class.

5. Start with an easy calculation such as 8 + 4 =. Set children the challenge of recording with a partner on a whiteboard all the ways that they can think of to represent this calculation.

6. Write their methods on the interactive whiteboard and discuss their merits.

7. Set the children off on the main activity with a time limit of about 20 minutes. Stress the importance of drawing calculations and emphasise that there are many ways to add one number to another.

Developing reasoning

➤ *In what other way could you add 45 to 28?* **Another, another, another.**
➤ *Can you partition 45 into other smaller numbers?* (not just tens and units)

➤ *Can you **convince me** that your ways of calculating are different? How are they different?*
➤ ***What's the same? What's different*** *about your ways of calculating?*
➤ Hold up two calculations in front of the class. ***What do you notice*** *about these calculations?*

Providing differentiation

Support
Provide children with a smaller calculation to work on first.

Extension
As adding 45 can be done in endless ways, e.g. 45 lots of 1, 4 tens and 5 ones, 5 eights, a 2 and a 3, this means that you can always ask for 'another, another, another'. Challenge children to come up with ten different ways of adding 45 to 28.

Key strategies

2   Another, another, another
3   Convince me
10 What do you notice?
12 What's the same? What's different?

Problem-solving approaches

Working in pairs

Taking it further

Every time the children work something out, ask them to do the same calculation in another way. This will encourage numerical reasoning and flexibility in calculations.

3 | The story of 20

Learning objective
- To add, subtract, multiply and divide numbers.

Reasoning skills
- Working systematically
- Solving problems
- Finding all possibilities
- Reasoning numerically

Curriculum link
1,3 Number: addition and subtraction, multiplication and division

The problem

Problem 3

The story of 20

20 is a useful number to be able to use.

It is exactly double 10.

You can multiply it to equal 100.

It is in the 2, 4, 5 and 10 times tables.

If you can find pairs of numbers that equal 20, then you can find pairs of numbers to almost anything.

Things to think about

- Can you work systematically and follow a pattern?
- Can you try adding and subtracting in the same calculation?

Your challenge

> **Tell your own story of the number 20.**
> **How many ways can you make 20?**
> **Use addition, subtraction, multiplication and division to help you reach the number 20.**
> **Be as creative as you can!**

20 20 **20** 20 20 20
20 *20*
20 **20** 20

Year 2

Problem Solving and Reasoning

Background knowledge

- This problem asks children to use different and numerous ways of making 20.
- 20 has three pairs of factors: 1 and 20, 2 and 10, 4 and 5. Two of them, 2 × 10 and 4 x 5, are facts from the 2, 5 and 10 times tables which are focal points in the Year 2 programme of study.
- Some children could use scaling to help them to find solutions to this problem, i.e. 40 ÷ 4 = 10, so 80 ÷ 4 = 20.

- To extend the challenge, the children could be encouraged to use negative numbers and fractions if they have some understanding of them.
- This problem has almost no end as you can always think of a two numbers that you can add together or subtract from each other to equal 20.

Launching the activity

1. Write a range of number sentences and representations of the number 12 on the board that use addition, subtraction, multiplication and division. Include pictures of 12 objects too.

2. Ask: *What do you notice?* and *What's the same? What's different?* about the calculations.

3. Elicit that they all equal the same number and that they are all ways of calculating using numbers to equal 12. Look for similarities in calculations, near numbers and number bonds to 10 too.

4. Share the poster with the children on the interactive whiteboard.

5. Ask children to talk to a partner about how they might make the number 20. Encourage them to be as creative as possible.

6. Listen to a few of their ideas and record them on the interactive whiteboard.

7. Set the children the challenge. Give them large pieces of paper and felt-tipped pens to record their ideas. Give them a time limit of 20 minutes to record their ideas.

8. Use a mini-plenary to refocus the children after five minutes. It is likely that they will find it difficult at first until they start to work in a systematic way.

9. Invite the children to share their 'Story of 20' with the rest of the class.

10. Attach their 'posters' to the working wall so that the children can add ideas to them throughout the week.

Developing reasoning

➤ *If you have used 19 + 1, and 18 + 2, what could you add to 17? Give me **another, another, another** similar calculation.*

➤ *If 2 × 5 = 10, what would 2 × 10 make?*

➤ ***If the answer is** 20, **what is the question?***

➤ ***What's the same? What's different** about the calculations that you have used so far?*

➤ *How can these calculations help you to find more?*

➤ ***What do you notice** about the number sentence that equals 12?*

Providing differentiation

Support
Give the children a single-digit number to work with initially before moving on to 20.

Extension
Challenge the children to use fractions, negative numbers and a greater amount of division in their calculations.

As an alternative, give children a low number that appears to be easy.

Key strategies

2 Another, another, another
5 If this is the answer, what is the question?
10 What do you notice?
12 What's the same? What's different?

Problem-solving approaches

Working systematically

Taking it further

Choose a 'number of the week' in the class. Put a large piece of paper on the working wall and invite the children to write their own story of the number on the paper during the week.

Learning objective
- To solve problems involving multiplication.
- To compare and order lengths.

Reasoning skills
- Making comparisons
- Making generalisations
- Solving problems

Curriculum link
1̲23 Number: multiplication

᷉᷉᷉ Measurement: comparing length

The problem

Double your robot

Your teacher has made a robot made from interlocking cubes.

The robot's feet are each made from 2 cubes and so are its legs.

Its body is made from a square of 9 cubes.

Each arm is an L-shape that is made from 4 cubes.

The neck is 1 cube and the head is an oblong made from 6 cubes.

The robot is 8 cubes tall and 5 cubes wide (including its arms.)

Things to think about

- In what way are you going to double the robot?
- How many cubes will you need for each part of its body?
- Make sure that you stick to your strategy, i.e. if you are doubling height, always double width.

Your challenge

Make the robot's big brother who is double the size of your teacher's robot.

Remember: You have to follow the same design and double the size. You can double a 3-D object in different ways: double the height, double the width, double the depth or double them all.

RISING STARS
Maths

Year 2   *Problem Solving and Reasoning*

Problem 4

Background knowledge

- The children are challenged to create a robot that is double the size of their teacher's robot.
- Following the same design, the 3-D robot could be doubled in different ways: by doubling its height, its width, its depth or by doubling it in every direction.
- The problem can be adapted for any model made with interlocking cubes. They key element is that the model is easy to replicate.
- A correct solution to this problem could involve the doubling of the robot in any direction, as the challenge is non-specific.
- If you double the robot in all directions, you replace each cube with 8 cubes, essentially

cubing the original dimensions (doubling the height turns 1 cube into 2, doubling the 2 (the new width) will give 4, then doubling again (the new depth) gives 8 cubes.) This is way beyond the Year 2 programme of study, so doubling in one direction is acceptable.

- To promote reasoning, encourage children to explain in what way they have doubled the robot.
- To tackle the challenge successfully, children will require the support of frequent mini-plenaries to scaffold their thinking and help them to stay on track.

Launching the activity

1. Join two interlocking cubes together. Then make a separate tower of four interlocking cubes.

2. Ask: *What do you notice?* Try to encourage children to realise that the tower of four cubes is double the length of the tower of two cubes.

3. Ensure that children understand the concept of doubling. Link it to halving and work through some similar examples with the children making towers that are double of half of the length of the towers that you show them.

4. Share the poster with the children.

5. Using interlocking cubes, build the robot as outlined on the poster. As you do this, describe the dimensions of the robot's body parts so that children become familiar with the robot's dimensions.

6. Set the challenge and answer any questions. Ensure that children understand that they can double the robot in any way that they like. This problem works well with children working in mixed-ability pairs.

7. Use mini-plenaries to focus the children on doubling the robot's dimensions.

8. After about 20 minutes, ask the children to place all their robots on a table so that you can compare them with the original robot.

9. Look together at each robot. Ask: *What's the same? What's different about each robot compared with the original?*

Developing reasoning

➤ *What do you notice* about the number of cubes needed for the second tower of cubes compared with the first tower?

➤ *What's the same? What's different* about the first robot and the doubled robot?

➤ *Convince me* or a partner that your robot is double the size of the original one. How do you know?

➤ *Can you double your robot in a way that no one else will? How is it different?*

Providing differentiation

Support
Sit with the children and help them to check that each part of their robot is the correct dimension.

Extension
Challenge the children to double the dimensions of the robot in more than one way. Can they make a robot that is half the size of one that you give them?

Key strategies

3 Convince me
10 What do you notice?
12 What's the same? What's different?

Problem-solving approaches

Working systematically
Mixed-ability pairs

Taking it further
Encourage the children to make other shapes with interlocking cubes. Ask: *How can you change its size?*

Learning objective
- To identify that addition and subtraction are inverses of each other.
- To find out if both addition and subtraction can be done in any order.

Reasoning skills
- Using numerical reasoning
- Spotting patterns
- Working systematically
- Finding all possibilities

Curriculum link
123 Number: addition and subtraction

The problem

> **Problem 5**
>
> ### Calculation families
>
> A calculation family is made up of four number sentences that all use the same numbers: two use addition, and two use subtraction. For example:
>
> | |
> |---|
> | $2 + 3 = 5$ |
> | $3 + 2 = 5$ |
> | $5 - 2 = 3$ |
> | $5 - 3 = 2$ |
>
> Can you make the families for these number sentences?
> 1) $4 + 16 = 20$
> 2) $100 - 70 = 30$
> 3) $12 + 5 + 3 = 20$
> 4) $25 + 30 + 20 + 25 = 100$
>
> **Your challenge**
>
> **Find all the members of the calculation families for each number sentence.**
> **Can you make your own number sentence families?**
>
> **Remember: Make sure that you find each solution.**
>
> **Things to think about**
> - Will it help you to focus on one operation first? Perhaps focusing on addition first and then subtraction?
> - Will you start with any particular number or sequence of numbers?
> - How many things will you change at a time?
> - How many different number sentences will be in an 'extended' number sentence family?
>
> RISING STARS **Maths**
>
> Year 2 — *Problem Solving and Reasoning*

Background knowledge

- The children are asked to find all of the members of calculation families for different number sentences. In the process, they will identify whether both addition and subtraction can be calculated in any order.
- Addition is commutative, subtraction is not.
- A commutative operation is one in which the order of combining two objects does not matter so can be described by $(a + b) = (b + a)$. This, in turn, means that $(a + b)$ is equal to $(b + a)$, i.e. $2 + 3 = 3 + 2$.
- Subtraction is not commutative as $(a - b) \neq (b - a)$, e.g $4 - 1$ does not equal $1 - 4$.

- Inverses are not opposites. The best way to consider an inverse is that it 'reverses' the operation: $1 + 3 = 4$, so if we reverse the operation, $4 - 3 = 1$.
- This problem should be quite straightforward for the first two examples as the children follow the structure outlined on the poster. Ensure, however, that children identify that the second example is a subtraction calculation and not an addition.
- The second two calculations are more challenging as there are more solutions to find that will not follow the structure that the children are used to.

Launching the activity

1. Remind the children about inverses, what it means and give an example.

2. Reveal on the interactive whiteboard Resource sheet 5.1, Inverse calculations: Ask: *What do you notice?* and *What's the same? What's different?* Encourage children to identify inverses and to recognise that one number sentence is the reverse of another. (In the case of finding the subtraction number sentence to match the addition one, $2 + 3 = 5$, the inverse would be $5 - 3 = 2$).

3. Emphasise that $2 + 3 = 5$ and $3 + 2 = 5$ are part of the 'family' but are not inverses. They just show that addition is commutative. Also focus on having the same numbers in the number sentence but having a different order and different symbols.

4. Demonstrate this by asking the children to hold physical digits and symbols, then change the order of the children and replace an addition sign for a subtraction sign.

5. Share the poster with the children. Discuss how a 'family' is made up and give examples, including the one on the poster.

6. Discuss the need to work systematically and to focus on one number operation at a time to ensure that you have all the solutions for each one before progressing. Set the children off on the challenge.

7. If the children bring incomplete solutions to you (especially for problems 3 and 4), ask for another another, another. If they say they have found all of the solutions, say, *Convince me.*

8. Bring the class together at the end of the lesson to share their solutions.

9. Ask: *Are both addition and subtraction commutative?*

Developing reasoning

➤ *What do you notice* about the number sentences $1 + 2 = 3$ and $3 - 2 = 1$?
➤ *What's the same? What's different* about the number sentences that you have written?
➤ *Can you a number sentence that is in the 'extended' number family? Another, another, another.*
➤ *Convince me* that you have you have found all of the members of the family. How do you know that you have?
➤ Give me a *silly answer* for a member of this calculation family. Why is it silly?

Providing differentiation

Support
Have number sentences on pieces of card for children to match up, rather that working in a more abstract way with digits.

Organise the children into mixed-ability groups to provide support.

Extension
Challenge children to come up with their own extended number families using more than three numbers, e.g. $1 + 2 + 3 = 6$ etc.

Key strategies

2 Another, another, another
3 Convince me
9 Silly answers
10 What do you notice?
12 What's the same? What's different?

Problem-solving approaches

Working systematically
Mixed-ability groups

Taking it further

Ask the children what other things come in families. Suggestions could include shapes and multiplication and division number sentences. Give examples of these appropriate for the children.

6 Put it in the right place!

Learning objective
- To use place value to solve problems.

Reasoning skills
- Solving problems
- Conjecturing and convincing
- Using numerical reasoning
- Spotting patterns and relationships

Curriculum link
1,3 Number: properties of number

The problem

Put it in the right place!

There are only ten digits but we can make every number in the world with them!

Where you place these digits will decide how big or small the number is and whether the number is more or less than another number.

If you only had one digit, could you find its missing partner?

Which digits are missing from these numbers?

23   27   2_   30   _4   46

Your challenge

Work out the missing digit in a 2-digit number.

Remember: **The numbers in the list are in order!**

Things to think about

- Is there more than one digit that you could use for each solution?
- Look at the numbers around the missing digit. Does the number need to be bigger or smaller?
- Do the numbers in the ordered list go up or down?
- How many tens and how many units are needed?

Year 2

Problem Solving and Reasoning

Background knowledge

- The children are asked to identify the missing digit in a 2-digit number.
- Stressing the place of the digit in each example in this problem is of paramount importance. The 2014 National Curriculum defines the places as Hundreds, Tens and Ones.
- Our number system, (which is the Hindu-Arabic number system) is in base ten, so to focus on 10 as the size of a set is a useful way to develop children's understanding.

- 123 could be described as being made up from 1 hundred, 2 tens and 3 'left over', thereby emphasising that we are making the 'ones' into sets of 10 before we place a digit in the second (tens) column.
- This problem will give lots of opportunities for using the strategies 'convince me' and 'another, another, another', as well as asking the questions 'What's the same? What's different?'

Launching the activity

1. Gather the necessary resources for the task: interlocking cubes, large pieces of paper, marker pens and Resource sheet 6.1, Place value problems.

2. Explain that this problem is all about place value. The children will need to focus on what each digit in a number stands for to solve the problems.

3. On a whiteboard, write 12 and 21. Ask the children: *What do you notice?* and *What's the same? What's different?* Focus on the place value of each digit. In 12 the digit 1 represents 1 ten, however, in 21 it represents 1. The opposite is true of the digit 2. They are the same in that they both has a 2 and a 1 and that they are 2-digit numbers. Also ask: *Which number is bigger than the other? How do you know?* The answer is that 21 is bigger because it has 2 tens whereas in 12 there is only 1 ten.

4. Give the children three digit cards. Ask what 2-digit numbers they can make from them. Discuss the relative size of each and the importance of place value. Use place value cards to highlight the structure.

5. Share the poster problem. Talk through the example given on it and discuss possible solutions (28 or 29, 34 or 44).

6. Set the children a range of problems that are similar to the one on the poster. Encourage them to discuss the relative size of the numbers and come up with multiple solutions by saying, *another, another, another.*

7. Bring the class together at the end of the lesson to share their solutions.

8. Challenge the children to 'convince me' that the numbers that they are suggesting are correct.

Developing reasoning

➤ *What do you notice* about the size of the numbers? Do they get bigger or smaller?
➤ *What's the same? What's different* about the numbers? Where are the digits and what do they represent?
➤ *Convince me* or a partner that you have found all of the possible solutions.
➤ Can you find a possible solution to this problem? *Another, another, another.*

Providing differentiation

Support
Vary the size and complexity of the problems that you give to the children. Provide cards with possible solutions on so that they can choose the best one.

Extension
Extend the challenge to 3-digit numbers and problems that have more possible solutions.

Key strategies

2 Another, another and another
3 Convince me
10 What do you notice?
12 What's the same? What's different?

Problem-solving approaches

Graffiti maths
Working in pairs

Taking it further

Place lists of numbers on the board for early work. Highlight one of the digits. Ask the children: *What other digits could you place here to keep the order of the numbers correct?*

Learning objective	**Reasoning skills**	**Curriculum link**
• To make totals of money.	• Solving problems • Working systematically • Making generalisations • Using numerical reasoning	**1₂³** Number: addition and subtraction **📊** Measurement: money

The problem

Problem 7

Moneybox puzzle

Your moneybox has a total of £1.00 in it.

However, you can't take it out unless you can say which coins are inside the moneybox.

You know that there are more than two coins by the sound that they make when you shake the moneybox.

What combinations of coins might be in your moneybox?

Things to think about

- What is the biggest value coin that could be in your moneybox?
- Can you work systematically and follow a pattern?
- What coin value will you start with?

Your challenge

Find all the combinations of coins that could be inside the moneybox

Remember: **There are many ways to total £1. You can use as many coins as you need to, as long as they total £1.**

RISING STARS
Maths

Year 2

Problem Solving and Reasoning

Background knowledge

- The children are challenged to find all the possible combinations of coins inside a moneybox.
- Working systematically is the only way to find all of the solutions to this problem.
- They should start with two lots of 50p, then one 50p, two lots of 20p and a 10p. Then one 50p, one 20p and three lots of 10p. They then continue in this way, always ensuring that they have the highest value coin first. Once they have exhausted all possible combinations with a 50p, they should place a 20p first and start again.

- Consider 1 × 50p, 2 × 20p and 1 × 10p to be the same as 1 × 50p, 1 ×10p and 2 × 20p. Point out that using the same coins in any order has to be considered to be the same solution; otherwise this problem would become very long and very complex.
- Recording children's solutions to the problem should be done in a systematic way to ensure all the solutions are found.

Launching the activity

1. Give the children one of each denomination of British coins (either real or replica). Challenge them to place them in an order of their choosing.

2. Refine the activity by asking the children to order the coins by their monetary value. This will provide many opportunities for asking reasoning-based questions.

3. Confirm the denominations of the coins and their respective values.

4. Write 20 on the board. Challenge children to write down different ways of making a total of 20. For example, 15 + 5 = 20, 15 + 3 + 2 = 20, etc.

5. Challenge the children to make a total of 20p with their British coins. Ask: *What do you notice?*

6. Share the problem poster. Ensure that all the children know that £1 is made up of 100p. Have a moneybox or tin containing £1 made from a selection of different coins. Shake it so that children can hear the coins and estimate how many coins might be inside. (Remind them that the box contains more than two coins.)

7. Discuss possible methods of finding the solutions. Steer the conversations towards starting with the 50p and emphasise working in a systematic way. Highlight that a 'scatter gun' approach would find solutions but would not ensure that you had found all of them.

8. Set the children off on their challenge. Suggest that they record their solutions by drawing around coins or writing strings of coins on paper.

9. After 20 minutes, regroup the class and share their solutions. Open the moneybox to show how many coins were actually in it.

Developing reasoning

➤ *Can you think of another combination of coins that could be inside?* **Another, another, another.**
➤ **Convince me** *that you have found all of the possible solutions.*
➤ **What do you notice** *about the way that I have recorded the possible combinations of coins that I have written on the board?* (They have been written it in a systematic way.)
➤ *Can you think of a really complicated combination of coins?*
➤ *What combinations can you find that use exactly seven coins?*
➤ *Give me a* **silly answer** *for the coins that could be in the box. Why is it silly?*

Providing differentiation

Support
Change the amount of money that the children are trying to find solutions to.

Extension
Ask the children to pick one solution from their list and justify it as the correct solution. This may be based on the number of coins that they think are in the moneybox or its mass.

 Key strategies

2 Another, another, another
3 Convince me
9 Silly answers
10 What do you notice?

 Problem-solving approaches

Working systematically

Taking it further

Place two 2-D shapes in a closed box. Tell the children that there are two shapes inside and that they have 7 sides between them. Ask: *What shapes could be inside the box?* (Repeat for 3-D shapes.)

Wheely puzzle

Learning objective
- To find different ways of making totals.
- To add and subtract numbers using concrete objects, pictorial representations, and mentally.

Reasoning skills
- Finding all possibilities
- Using numerical reasoning

Curriculum link
1,3 Number: addition and subtraction

.il Measurement: money

The problem

Problem 8a

Wheely puzzle

A unicycle has just 1 wheel. A bike has 2 wheels.

A trike has 3 and a car has 4.

What has 5 wheels? How about 6 or 7?

Things to think about

- 1 car + 1 bike + 1 unicycle = 7 wheels, so do 3 bikes and a unicycle.
- Can you make the numbers in a different way?

Your challenge

Find how many numbers you can make by adding the numbers of wheels on each vehicle.

Which number can you make the highest number of different additions for?

Remember: There will be more than one way to make each number. Work systematically and start with the lowest number of wheels.

RISING STARS
Maths

Year 2 — *Problem Solving and Reasoning*

Background knowledge

- This problem encourages children to find multiple ways of finding totals. Rather than rushing on to the next calculation or in this case, target number, mathematical thinking can be developed by finding the target number in another way. For example, 7 = 4 + 3 and 7 = 4 + 2 + 1 and 7 = 3 + 2 + 2 etc. There will be many ways to make numbers, particularly as the target numbers get bigger.
- This problem can also help to explore the concept of addition being a commutative operation, which means that addition can be calculated in any order, e.g. 1 + 2 = 2 + 1.
- The table details the numbers of wheels and a corresponding vehicle that could be used in the

context of the problem. If necessary, these can be changed to suit the interests of children.

Number of wheels	Suggested vehicle
1	Unicycle
2	Bike (or bicycle, motorbike)
3	Trike (or tricycle)
4	Car (or van, tractor)
6	Lorry

- To keep the problem as simple as possible, the children should consider 2 cars + 1 bike to be the same solution as 1 bike + 2 cars.

Launching the activity

1. Write 5 on the board. Ask the children to write down a number sentence that will equal 5, e.g. $1 + 4 = 5$. Take some suggestions, then ask for 'another, another, another'. Encourage children to realise that they can use more than two numbers to make a total, e.g. $5 = 2 + 2 + 1$.

2. Show the vehicles on poster 8b. As you point to each vehicle, say the number that corresponds to the number of wheels it has. For example, as you point to the bike, say 2, (not 2 wheels), as you point to the car, say 4. Ask: *What do you notice?* Elicit that the numbers you say relate to the number of wheels on each vehicle.

3. Once the children have made the connection between the vehicle and the number of wheels, ask a few addition problems such as, 1 car + 1 bike = ? or 2 bikes + 1 lorry = ?

4. Share the poster problem and explain the challenge.

5. Encourage the children to work systematically, first using a unicycle to represent 1. Then move on to making 2 by using a bike OR 2 unicycles to emphasise the need to find multiple ways of making each number.

6. Working in pairs helps children to generate solutions and provides opportunities to share conjectures.

7. While the children are finding solutions, promote mathematical thinking by prompting them for 'another, another, another' solution.

8. At the end of the lesson, choose a number and ask the children to share all the different ways they found to make it. Ask: *Have we found them all? How could we check?*

Developing reasoning

➤ *Can you find another way of making 5 wheels?* **Another, another, another.**
➤ *Can you make the number 9 from only bicycles? Why not?*
➤ *Are 2 cars and 1 trike equal to 5 bicycles? How do you know?*
➤ **What do you notice** *about the solutions for even numbers of wheels compared with those for odd numbers of wheels?* (You can't make odd numbers without a unicycle or a trike.)

Providing differentiation

Support
Providing simple clipart cut-out pictures of the vehicles will help children to create different numbers of wheels in a physical way. These could then be stuck down on a large piece of paper.

Extension
If children keep finding a single combination for each number of wheels, encourage them to find more combinations that equal the same total, rather than just finding combinations for higher numbers, e.g. 1 trike + 1 car = 3 bikes + 1 unicycle.

 Key strategies

2   Another, another, another
10 What do you notice?

 Problem-solving approaches

Working in pairs

Taking it further

Challenge children to find a different theme for a similar problem such as; 1 = your nose, 2 = your eyes, 5 = your toes, etc.

9 A difference of 5

Learning objective
- To find multiple solutions to a problem.

Reasoning skills
- Using numerical reasoning
- Spotting patterns and relationships
- Solving problems

Curriculum link
1,2,3 Number: addition and subtraction

The problem

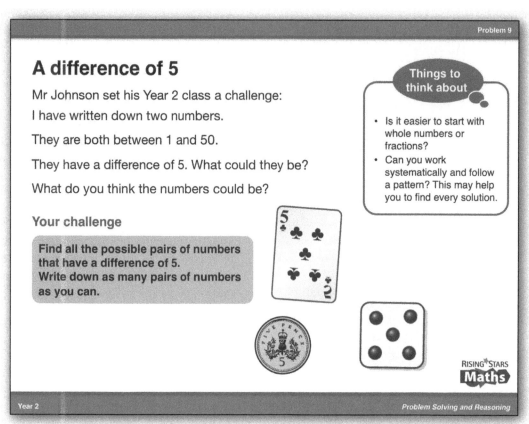

Problem 9

A difference of 5

Mr Johnson set his Year 2 class a challenge:

I have written down two numbers.

They are both between 1 and 50.

They have a difference of 5. What could they be?

What do you think the numbers could be?

Things to think about
- Is it easier to start with whole numbers or fractions?
- Can you work systematically and follow a pattern? This may help you to find every solution.

Your challenge

Find all the possible pairs of numbers that have a difference of 5.
Write down as many pairs of numbers as you can.

Year 2

Problem Solving and Reasoning

RISING STARS
Maths

Background knowledge

- The children are asked to find all possible pairs of numbers that have a difference of 5.
- There are a high number of solutions to this problem. Encourage children to find as many as they can.

- The children should be encouraged to work systematically so that they can find all of the solutions: 1 and 6, 2 and 7, 3 and 8, etc.
- Identify the structure of this problem: 2 and 7 have a difference of 5 because both 2 and 7 are 2 greater than 0 and 5. This pattern continues as both numbers increase.

Launching the activity

1. Start the lesson by writing pairs of numbers on the board that have a difference of 1. Ask: *What do you notice?*

2. Challenge the children to come up with pairs of numbers that have a difference of 2. They should record these on their whiteboards then share them with the class. Show the importance of working systematically at this point.

3. Share the poster with the children and (secretly) write down your chosen pair of numbers.

4. Discuss some possible solutions to the problem. Then allow the children 20 minutes to generate as many solutions as they can, working in pairs and recording their solutions as graffiti maths. Most children will work with integers, however there is nothing to stop them using fractions of numbers.

5. As the children are generating solutions, ask them to provide a 'hard and easy' solution to the problem, e.g. 1 and 6 is an easy solution, $32\frac{1}{2}$ and $37\frac{1}{2}$ could be a hard one. Remind them to keep on working systematically. Also push the children to find 'another, another, another' solution.

6. Regroup the children and share their solutions with the whole class.

7. Show the children your chosen pair of numbers.

8. Finally, write on the board three numbers in a sequence with a difference of 10, e.g. 2, 12, 22. Ask, *Which one is the odd one out?* It could be: 2 because it is a single-digit number, 22 because both digits are the same, 12 because it has a 1 in it, 12 because it is 10 away from both other numbers etc.

Developing reasoning

> ➤ *What do you notice* about these pairs of numbers? (They have a constant difference.)
> ➤ *Convince me* that all of your pairs of numbers have a difference of 5.
> ➤ In the plenary, which of the three numbers is the *odd one out*?
> ➤ Can you find a different solution? *Another, another, another.*
> ➤ Give me a *silly answer* for two numbers that have a difference of 5. Why is it silly?
> ➤ If we know that 2 and 7 have a difference of 5, *what else do we know?*
> ➤ Can you find a *hard and easy* example?

Providing differentiation

Support
All the children should be able to come up with some solutions to this problem. Use the representation of a number line or a 1–100 square to scaffold children's understanding.

Extension
Introduce the idea of negative numbers and fractions of numbers. For example, –1 and 4 or $1\frac{1}{2}$ and $6\frac{1}{2}$.

Key strategies

2 Another, another, another
3 Convince me
4 Hard and easy
7 Odd one out
9 Silly answers
10 What do you notice?
11 What else do we know?

Problem-solving approaches

Graffiti maths
Conjecturing and convincing

Taking it further

This activity can be repeated in small amounts of time during the school day with any constant difference. This should be conducted in the form of 'another, another, another', e.g. You can go to line up for lunch if you can tell me two numbers that have a difference of 2.

10 Coin totals

Learning objective
- To combine amounts of money to make totals.

Reasoning skills
- Using numerical reasoning
- Solving problems
- Spotting patterns

Curriculum link
- 📊 Money: total amounts of money using symbols

The problem

Problem 10a

Coin totals

The coins used in Britain are: 1p, 2p, 5p, 10p, 20p, 50p, £1 and £2.

We can use different combinations of coins to pay for things in shops, but what if you only had one of each coin?

Your challenge

> Work out how many amounts between 1p and £1 you can you make if you only have one of each coin.

Things to think about

- If you can make 3p with 1p + 2p, does this help you make 8p by adding just one more coin?
- Is it easier to start with the bigger or smaller coins?
- Can you work systematically to help you find all possible solutions?

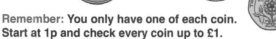

Remember: You only have one of each coin.
Start at 1p and check every coin up to £1.
It will not be possible to make every amount of money.

Year 2   *Problem Solving and Reasoning*

Background knowledge

- Children will need to be familiar with British coins to attempt this challenge which is to make amounts between 1p and £1 with only one of each coin.
- The denominations of the coins that are used in the United Kingdom have been carefully chosen. Following the pattern 1, 2, 5 means that you can make any amount with the smallest number of coins, e.g. 9p can be made from 1 ×5p, 2 ×2p and 1 ×1p. This pattern continues in the tens with 10p, 20p, 50p.
- Identifying patterns in the coin values will help children to work systematically:
  - 1p + 2p = 3p so 10p + 20p = 30p

  - If you have made 3p, you can then add it to 5p to make 8p.
  - This can then be applied to adding 30p to 50p to make 80p.
- As you cannot make 4p with only one of each coin, neither can you make 9p, 14p or 19p. You can make multiples of 5 with a 5p or 10p, but with a 1p and 2p you cannot make 4p, therefore you cannot make a multiple of 5p + 4p, such as 9p or 14p.
- This also applies to tens; as you cannot make 40p, you cannot make any amount of money from 39p and 49p.
- You can make any number that is either 1p, 2p or 3p more than a multiple of 5.

Launching the activity

1. Using large coins, play a 'guess my coin' game. Model it first before a child takes your role. With one coin in a bag or behind a screen, describe its size, shape and colouring. Ask: *Which coin is it?* Repeat for each coin.

2. Share the poster and ask: *If you had a 1p, a 2p and a 5p, what amounts could you make?* Give children three minutes to come up with all of the amounts that they can make using just these three coins. Discuss the issues they encounter, e.g. not being able to make 4p or 9p. *What do you notice about the amounts that you can make and those that you can't make?* (They should be able to make 1p, 2p, 3p, 5p, 6p, 7p and 8p.) *Why do you think that you can't make 4p or 9p?*

3. With the children in groups of three or four, assign each group a range of numbers between 1 and 100. Less able children could start with 1–20, the next group 21–40, then 41–60 etc. Children could record their solutions by drawing coins, writing number sentences (1p + 2p + 5p = 8p) or by arranging coins and photographing the result. Alternatively, provide a 100p square (a 100-square with a 'p' after each number to make it pence). Children then colour in the amounts they can make and leave those they cannot make blank.

4. Ensure the children work systematically. Start with the lowest number in the group's range and use the biggest coin they can first. So, working with 61p–80p, they would try to make 61p first and start with a 50p, add a 10p then a 1p.

5. Finally, invite groups to present their results to the rest of the class. Ask them to reason why they cannot make certain numbers and convince the rest of the class with their conjectures.

Developing reasoning

➤ *Why do you think that you can't make 4p or 9p?* (See background knowledge.)
➤ *What patterns can you see in the solutions that you have found?*
➤ ***Convince me*** *that you can or cannot make 49p with one of each coin.*
➤ ***What do you notice*** *about the order that you have written the coins down in? Why is it good to use the largest coin first?*
➤ *What is the largest amount you can make with one of each coin to 50p?*

Providing differentiation

Support
The children would benefit from using coins to support their reasoning. Recording can be pictorial or through photographs or by colouring amounts that can be made on a 1p to 100p square. (as mentioned above).

Extension
Ask the children to consider what amounts could be made that are greater than £1. *How are they the same or different to the solutions below £1? What if you also had a £1 and £2 coin as well. What amount can you make now?*

Key strategies
3 Convince me
10 What do you notice?

Problem-solving approaches
Working in groups

Taking it further

Expand the challenge by asking, *I have got 17p, how many ways can I make 17p? Can I make it with only one of each coin? Can I make it with two coins? Three coins? Four coins? Five coins? etc.* Of course, it is not possible with two coins, however asking them to do this will highlight that it is not possible.

11 Polyhedron Primary

Learning objective
- To recognise, describe and name common 3-D shapes.

Reasoning skills
- Making comparisons
- Conjecturing and convincing

Curriculum link
 Properties of shape: describe and sort 2-D and 3-D shapes

The problem

Problem 11

Polyhedron Primary

In the playground at Polyhedron Primary School, there are lots of 3-D shaped children running around!

When the headteacher, Mrs Tetrahedron, rings the bell for the end of playtime, she asks all of the shape children to get into lines of the same shape.

Things to think about
- What's the same?
- What's different?
- Which everyday objects are these shapes?
  - bean can = cylinder
  - dice = cube

Your challenge

Describe the properties of each 3-D shape.
How are 3-D shapes similar to each other?
How are they different from each other?

Remember: Use these words to describe the shapes: edge, face, vertex (or vertices if there is more than one).

RISING STARS
Maths

Year 2   Problem Solving and Reasoning

Background knowledge

- The challenge for children in this problem is to describe the properties of 3-D shapes.
- The online Oxford English Dictionary defines a polyhedron as 'A solid figure with many plane faces, typically more than six'. However, the term 3-D shape is widely understood to mean the same and will be more familiar to the children.
- Encourage the children to use the correct mathematical terms when describing 3-D shapes, i.e. edge, face and vertex/vertices rather than sides and corners.
- Correct definitions and names of 3-D shapes are important as children will remember the

terminology that is used in KS1 throughout their school life. Start with cubes, cuboids, spheres (not balls), cones, and square-based pyramids. Then introduce triangular prisms (and other prisms if they are available) and dodecahedrons. Encourage children to research their own 3-D shapes.

- Using interlocking 2-D shapes or other construction equipment to create 3-D shapes is a great way of encouraging children to investigate 3-D shape and will lead to them wanting to research an unknown shape that they have just made.

Launching the activity

1. Pass around everyday objects such as baked bean cans, tubes of crisps, cereal boxes, triangular prism chocolate boxes, etc. Display similar images and provide 3-D shapes for children to manipulate. Ask: *What do you notice about the shapes of these containers?*

2. Set the scene by reading the information on the poster.

3. Give plastic 3-D shapes and food containers out to a selection of children, making sure that there is more than one of each type of shape.

4. Role play the scenario from the poster. *How did you know that the two cylinders should stand next to each other?* Discuss 'what's the same?' and 'what's different?' about one of the shapes compared with the similar food containers.

5. Allow the children to 'think, pair, share' as they record their ideas with their partner. Record the children's conjectures on the interactive whiteboard as this will encourage further participation from other children.

6. Print out the page and put it on your working wall as a prompt for further discussion; children may wish to add to it later on during the week.

7. Give out Resource sheet 11.1, 3-D shapes. Ask: *Which shapes are they? How do you know?* Children cut out and sort the shapes in pairs.

8. As a plenary, reveal parts of a 3-D shape to the children. Can they guess which shape you are showing them? How do they know which shape is it? Try to show the 3-D shapes from unusual orientations to promote visualisation.

Developing reasoning

➤ *What's the same? What's different about two of the shapes?*
➤ *How did you know that the two cylinders should stand next to each other?*
➤ *What makes this shape a (insert name of shape)?*
➤ *Give me a strange, obvious and general shape with six faces.*
➤ *Draw a strange and obvious shape with more than six edges.*

Providing differentiation

Support
Ensure that all children are supported with specific 3-D shape language. All the children should have access to the 3-D representations of the shapes and the food containers.

Extension
Ask children to use interlocking 2-D shapes to make a new 3-D shape and then describe its features to a friend. They could also investigate different ways of sorting the shapes, e.g. all shapes with triangular faces in one line. Challenge them to think of a way of grouping them that no one else will think of.

 Key strategies

8 Strange and obvious
10 What do you notice?
11 What else do we know?
12 What's the same? What's different?

 Problem-solving approaches

Working in pairs
Think, pair, share

Taking it further

Ask the children to look around the classroom. *What shapes can you see?* Ask them to make a collection of 3-D shapes and to name them. *What's the same? What's different about two of the shapes?*

Learning objective
- To solve problems using multiplication and arrays.

Reasoning skills
- Conjecturing and convincing
- Using numerical reasoning
- Solving problems
- Working systematically

Curriculum link
1,3 Multiplication and division: using arrays

The problem

Problem 12a

The lunchbox trolley

In Miss Christie's class, there are 24 children.

All children bring a lunchbox to school, so Miss Christie needs somewhere to store them.

The caretaker has said that she will build a storage trolley for the lunchboxes but doesn't know how to arrange them.

How could the lunchboxes be arranged to fit in a rectangular trolley?

Your challenge

Find all the possible ways of arranging 24 cubes so that they would fit in a rectangular trolley.
Can you convince your teacher that your arrangement is the best?

Remember: Every lunchbox is a cube and the base of each one is a square. The trolley has to be a rectangle.
The lunchboxes cannot be placed on top of each other in case one of them breaks!

Things to think about

- Can you use cubes to help you make different arrangements of lunchboxes?
- Did you know that rectangles can be long or short and thin or wide?
- Can you work in a systematic way to find all of the solutions?

RISING STARS
Maths

Year 2

Problem Solving and Reasoning

Background knowledge

- The children are asked to find arrays that contain 24 cubes. There are eight solutions to this problem if you include both 1 × 24 and 24 × 1. They are:
  1 × 24, 2 × 12, 3 × 8, 4 × 6, 6 × 4, 8 × 3, 12 × 2, 24 × 1.
- Arrays represent multiplication or division well as they show in pictorial form what 4 lots of 6 or 6 lots of 4 actually look like.

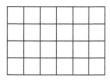

- You can read a multiplication number sentence in two ways: 4 × 6 could be '4 lots of 6' or it could be '4, 6 times'. It also depends on whether you are thinking in rows or columns.
- Arrays are made from rows (horizontal) and columns (vertical). When describing the additive nature of multiplication, be consistent in the language that you use. For instance, the array on the left could be described as 4 lots of 6, because there are 4 columns of 6.
- It may be tempting to stack the lunchboxes in the shape of a cuboid (2 × 3 on the base and 4 boxes high), however this is beyond the expectations for Year 2. This could be an adaptation of the problem for older children.

Launching the activity

1. Display poster 12b and ask: *What do you notice?* Elicit that each shape shows 12 but in different ways. Also highlight that 3 × 4 and 4 × 3 are the same shape, just orientated differently. Introduce the term array and, if necessary, explain what it is.

2. Put the children into pairs and give each pair 16 interlocking cubes. Ask: *If these cubes were the square lunchboxes, how could you arrange them into an array?* Discuss their suggestions and record them on the interactive whiteboard. Print the page and post it on the working wall so that children can refer to it.

3. Share the main poster and discuss the challenge. Ensure that the children make the link between the square lunchboxes and the cubes and that the solutions that they are looking for are in the form of arrays. Remind them that once they have found all of the solutions, they should decide which would be best and know why.

4. Give each child 24 cubes and enough time to complete the challenge. Remind them to work systematically, e.g. start with 1 × 24, then 2 × 12 etc.

5. The children could record their solutions with drawings, number sentences or photographs of their arrays.

6. Regroup the children and discuss their solutions. *Which array would be best for the design of the lunchbox trolley? Why do you think this?*

Developing reasoning

➤ *What's the same? What's different* about the arrays that you have created?
➤ How did working systematically help you to find all of the solutions?
➤ *What do you notice* about the arrays on the poster?
➤ Show me an array you have found for the 24 lunchboxes. *Another, another, another.*
➤ If we know that we can arrange the cubes in this way [pick a solution given by the child], *what else do we know?*

Providing differentiation

Support
Ensure that all children are supported with access to 24 cubes. Alternatively, children could make and record arrays easily by cutting them out of squared paper and sticking them down on a piece of coloured paper.

Extension
Challenge the children to create different arrays. Ask: *How would you change your arrays if 1 child joined the class? How about if 4 children joined the class?*

 Key strategies

2   Another, another, another
10 What do you notice?
12 What's the same? What's different?

 Problem-solving approaches

Working in pairs

Taking it further

Set up 48 interlocking cubes on a table at the side of the classroom. Challenge the children to arrange them in as many different arrays as possible. They should draw the arrays that they make. Can they make the link with multiplication?

Learning objective
- To solve problems involving time.

Reasoning skills
- Conjecturing and convincing
- Using numerical reasoning
- Solving problems
- Working systematically

Curriculum link
📊 Time: compare and sequence intervals of time

¹⁄₂ Addition and subtraction: add time periods

The problem

Lunchtime fun

What do you do at lunchtime?

Eat your lunch, have a drink, play football, practise your spellings, talk to your friends, run around, read a book … .

You have 60 minutes. What are you going to do?

Your challenge

Work out how many activities you can do in your lunchtime of 60 minutes.
How many activities can you pack into 60 minutes?
Which order will you do the activities in?

Remember: **You can do an activity more than once during your lunchtime.**
You can play football twice or talk to your friend three times.
You can do a few activities or lots of different ones. It's up to you as long as they add up to 60 minutes.

Things to think about
- Can you look for number bonds to make 10s numbers?
- Is it better to choose long or short activities?
- How many different activities could you fit into your 60 minutes?

RISING STARS
Maths

Year 2   *Problem Solving and Reasoning*

Background knowledge

- This problem is based on additive reasoning: addition and subtraction in the form of separating (partitioning) numbers, thinking of parts of numbers and comparing the relative sizes of numbers to find a best fit.
- In this problem, the children will need to identify activities that will fit together well to add up to an overall time of 60 minutes, using additive strategies of separating numbers and recombining them.
- Encourage the children to find number bonds in the ones place of the numbers to help them to make tens. This will help them to end up with a final total of 60 minutes of activity.

For example, playing football (12 minutes) and running around the playground (8 minutes) would add up to 20 minutes.

- Being able to read the time is not essential for this challenge. However children do need to be aware that there are 60 minutes in an hour and have a concept of the passing of time, e.g. 12 minutes to play football is longer than 3 minutes to line up for going outside. To reinforce this idea, create lists on the board of activities that might take 1 minute and those that might take 1 hour.

Launching the activity

1. Ask: *How long is five seconds? Ten seconds*?
   After discussing their suggestions, ask the children to close their eyes. When you say, *Go!*, the children should raise their hand when they think five seconds have elapsed. Use a stopwatch for accuracy. Do the same with ten seconds. How accurate were they?

2. Ask: *How many seconds are there in a minute?* Do the same activity for one minute.

3. Ask: *How many minutes are there in an hour? What things can you think of that might last for one minute or one hour?* Rephrase this as 60 minutes to show how the language is linked. Take suggestions and discuss.

4. Share the poster. Ensure that children understand the problem. Even though they are possible solutions, encourage children to plan a varied lunchtime rather than just 'reading a book' six times or 'having a drink' 60 times.

5. Display poster 13b and make sure that children know what each activity is and how long it takes. *What do you notice about how long each activity takes?* Allow 25 minutes for children to plan out their lunchtime using Resource sheets 13.1 and 13.2, Lunchtime fun..

6. There are two strategies they could use:
   - Plan a few activities that take longer amounts of time and then fill in the gaps with activities that take a shorter amount of time.
   - Make pairs of numbers that equal 10 or 20, e.g. skipping for 6 minutes and practising spellings for 4 minutes would equal 10 minutes.

7. Encourage the children to plan out several sets of activities. Set your own constraints such as adding or removing time, or adding new activities.

8. Bring the children together to share their lunchtime plans and explain their reasoning.

Developing reasoning

➤ *What do you notice* about how long each activity on the poster takes? (number bonds)
➤ *How could you use your knowledge of number bonds to help you make a total of 60 minutes?*
➤ *Which of the activities is the **odd one out**? Why?*
➤ *Give me a combination of activities that would last for 60 minutes. **Another, another, another**.*

Providing differentiation

Support
Provide pictures of the lunchtime activities with times on them. This will help some children to plan out a lunchtime that will last for 60 minutes.

Use poster Resource sheet 13.2 that have times in intervals of 5 minutes only.

Extension
Ask: *How would you change your lunchtime plan if you only had 45 minutes instead of 60?*

Adding new activities or constraints to the problem will prompt mathematical thinking and creativity.

Key strategies
2   Another, another, another
7   Odd one out
10 What do you notice?

Problem-solving approaches
Working in pairs

Taking it further

Ask the children, *What can you do in a minute? How many star jumps, hops or writing your own name?* Use a stopwatch (or a sand timer) to time different amounts of time (30 seconds, 45 seconds, 1 minute etc.) and ask, *What can you do in this time?*

Learning objective
- To solve problems by adding single-digit numbers.

Reasoning skills
- Using numerical reasoning
- Solving problems
- Finding all possibilities
- Working systematically

Curriculum link
1₂3 Number: addition and subtraction

The problem

Problem 14

Total patterns

Our number system works by only using ten digits.

These are the numbers 0, 1, 2, 3, 4, 5, 6, 7, 8, 9.

If you add three of these numbers that are consecutive, which numbers could you make?

Things to think about

- Can you use known number facts to help you?
- What addition strategies do you know?
- Which single-digit numbers would help you to make high or low totals?
- Can you find a pattern in the totals that you make?

Your challenge

Work out which numbers you can make by adding three consecutive single-digit numbers.

What's the highest total that you can make?

What's the lowest total that you can make?

Which numbers can you make if you use subtraction too?

Remember: Consecutive means that the numbers follow each other in order:

1, 2, 3 and 6, 7, 8 are consecutive numbers

2, 4, 7 are not consecutive numbers

RISING STARS
Maths

Year 2

Problem Solving and Reasoning

Background knowledge

- The children are asked to investigate adding consecutive single-digit numbers.
- Addition is commutative, subtraction is not. Commutative operations can be done in any order: A + B = B + A, whereas A – B ≠ B – A. E.g. 2 + 3 = 5, as does 3 + 2, whereas 6 – 2 = 4, but 2 – 6 does not equal 4.
- This highlights the ordinal aspect of numbers. Ordinal numbers tell the order of things in a set: first, second, third, fourth, etc. They do not show a quantity; they only show the rank or position, e.g. I came first in a race. In this case, by using the consecutive numbers 1, 2, 3, the problem is highlighting that 1 comes before 2, which is followed by 3.

- The table shows solutions to this problem if you only use addition:

Consecutive numbers	Total
0 1 2	3
1 2 3	6
2 3 4	9
3 4 5	12
4 5 6	15
5 6 7	18
6 7 8	21
7 8 9	24

- Using addition *and* subtraction will give many more possibilities. The challenge can then be extended to include: what numbers can you make/can't you make?

- The table shows that the totals, if calculated in that order, will have increments of 3. As there are three consecutive numbers in the calculation, each time you increase each number by 1. Therefore each total increases by 3 (3 × 1).

- Alternatively, if you take 1 away from the third number and add it to the first number, each number will be the same as the middle one.
- As the first middle number is a 1, then a 2, 3 etc., you will compile the three times table as you calculate each set of numbers.

Launching the activity

1. Give yourself and each child a number fan. Do a quick-fire warm-up based on holding up digits that are more or less than a given number. For example, hold up 4 and say, *Show me a single-digit number that is more than a 4.* Continue with numbers that are more and less but still single-digit numbers. Allow some confident children to take your role.

2. Write some single-digit numbers in groups of three on the interactive whiteboard. Some should be random, e.g. 4 5 8 or 8 2 4, others should be consecutive. Ask: *What do you notice?* Introduce the concept of consecutive numbers.

3. Share the poster. Ask the children to suggest three consecutive single-digit numbers. Use 'think, pair, share' for this. Record children's ideas on the interactive whiteboard.

4. Explain the problem. Emphasise that the numbers have to be single-digit and consecutive and that children are only using addition. Working systematically will ensure that children use all of the combinations of numbers.

5. Give each child a set of digit cards Resource sheet 14.1, Digit cards 1–30, a 1–30 number line, Resource sheet 12.2, Number line 1–30 (for support) and 20 minutes to complete the challenge. Mixed-ability groups work well for this problem.

6. Challenge the children to come up with several solutions. Finally, regroup the children to share their calculations. Ask: *What do you notice about the totals of the three numbers?*

Developing reasoning

➤ Is it **always, sometimes or never** true that when you add three consecutive numbers under 10, you get a number between 10 and 20?
➤ **What do you notice** about the number sentences that you have recorded? **What do you notice** about the totals?
➤ How could you use your knowledge of number bonds to help you to add the digits together?
➤ Which of your sets of three numbers is the **odd one out** and why?
➤ Can you add three consecutive numbers together to equal an even number?

Providing differentiation

Support
Sit with the children to ask questions that will help to develop reasoning. Provide number lines and counting resources (such as cubes) to aid their calculations.

Extension
Ask: *What totals can you make if you use the number operations of addition and subtraction? What numbers can't you make by using both number operations in the same calculation?*

 Key strategies

1 Always, sometimes, never
7 Odd one out
10 What do you notice?

Problem-solving approaches

Mixed-ability grouping

Taking it further

Repeat the activity but this time use 2-digit numbers. Ask: *Can you make the number 100 in this way? What about 101?*

Learning objective
- To find fractions of lengths and shapes.

Reasoning skills
- Solving problems
- Working systematically
- Making comparisons
- Spotting patterns and relationships

Curriculum link
1,3 Fractions: find fractions of lengths, quantities, sets of objects or shapes

The problem

The Fraction family

Mr Fraction is the tallest in the family.

Mrs Fraction is half the height of Mr Fraction.

Freddie, their son, is half the height of his mother.

Freya, the baby, is half the height of Freddie.

Fido, their pet guinea pig, is half the height of Freya.

Can you draw the Fraction family?

Things to think about

- If a quarter is half of a half, what would half of a quarter be?
- What does the denominator tell you?
- What does the numerator tell you?

Your challenge

Draw all the members of the Fraction family, each one on a their own strip of paper.

Describe the size of each family member compared with Mr Fraction and with each other.

Remember: **A half of a half is a quarter.**

A half is equal to two quarters.

Numerator means the top number.

Denominator means the bottom number.

RISING STARS
Maths

Year 2   *Problem Solving and Reasoning*

Background knowledge

- This problem highlights the relative sizes of fractions as fractions of the same 'whole'. Mr Fraction represents the 'whole', Mrs Fraction is one half of the whole, Freddie is a quarter of the whole, Freya is an eighth of the whole and Fido is a sixteenth. While there is no expectation to use eighths and sixteenths in Year 2, children can relate the size of Freya compared with Freddie as being 'half of the size'.

- Drawings for this activity can be done on separate pieces of paper so that the family can be laid out next to each other and stuck down. This approach helps children to make a fraction wall of sorts. The wall would show

that 4 Freddies are equal to 1 Mr Fraction as they could compare Freddie to Mr Fraction by laying them beside each other.

- The wall of drawings might look like this:

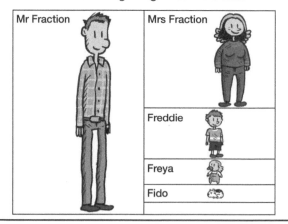

Launching the activity

1. Show the children poster 15b on the interactive whiteboard. Ask: *What do you notice?* Establish that they are all equal to a half. Extend to a quarter if appropriate.

2. Discuss the meaning of a half, how to find a half and what it might look like. Ask gchildren to draw their own representations of a half on whiteboards.

3. Share the poster and read through the description of the family. Answer any questions it raises.

4. Using a strip of paper 4cm wide, demonstrate how to draw Mr Fraction. Ensure that his head touches one end of the strip and his feet touch the other end. Each family member must be drawn in the same way, otherwise they will not be half the size of the previous one.

5. Ask: *How could we find half of Mr Fraction's height?* Use 'think, pair, share' to stimulate suggestions. Establish that the best way is to get a strip of paper that is the length of Mr Fraction and fold it in half. After cutting along the fold, you have a strip of paper that is the correct length. *How would we find half of Mrs Fraction's height?* Ensure that children realise that by folding the paper in half, they are finding half of the length of the previous family member.

6. In mixed-ability groups, set the children off on the challenge. Ensure that they also describe the height of each family member compared to another one.

7. As a mini-plenary, ask if the children can think of another way of finding half of Mr Fraction's height. One way would be to measure him and divide the measurement by 2. The same could then be done for each family member.

8. Finally, invite the children to show their fraction families and to explain how big each family member is compared to another one.

Developing reasoning

➤ *Is it **always, sometimes or never** true that the smaller the bottom number on a fraction, the smaller the fraction is?*
➤ ***What do you notice** about the representations on the poster? What do they all show?*
➤ *How big is Freddie compared to Mr Fraction?*
➤ *Which of the representations of a half is the **odd one out** and why?*
➤ *If Freddie's cousin Frankie is a quarter of the size of Mrs Fraction, who is he the same size as?*

Providing differentiation

Support
Provide a fraction wall for the children to see the relative size of the fractions. Some children may need help with the folding of the strips of paper accurately.

Extension
Can children create another fraction family that is based on thirds? For example, Mummy is the whole strip of paper, the first child is one third of her height, the baby is one third of the height of the child, etc.

 Key strategies

1 Always, sometimes, never
7 Odd one out
10 What do you notice?

 Problem-solving approaches

Mixed-ability grouping

Taking it further

Can children make their own fraction families based on other fractions? How about family members that are made of non-unit fractions such as $\frac{3}{4}$ or $\frac{2}{3}$?

<table>
<tr><td>

Learning objective
- To use mathematical vocabulary to describe position, direction and movement.

</td><td>

Reasoning skills
- Solving problems
- Working systematically

</td><td>

Curriculum link
- Position and direction: describe position and direction accurately

</td></tr>
</table>

The problem

Problem 16a

My robot friend

Robots are amazing!

They can do all sorts of fantastic things. They can build cars in factories, calculate with really big numbers and they can even walk like humans!

What they **ALL** have in common is that they do **EXACTLY** what they are told to do.

Do you think that you could control a robot?

Your challenge

> Give instructions to a friend to move like a robot through an obstacle course.
>
> If you are the robot, you must follow your instructions exactly.

Remember: **A quarter turn is the same as a right angle turn. Give very clear and precise instructions. Robots do EXACTLY what they are told.**

Things to think about
- What direction is clockwise?
- What direction is anticlockwise?
- What type of information do you need to give to your partner?

RISING STARS
Maths

Year 2 — Problem Solving and Reasoning

Background knowledge

- The children are challenged to instruct a friend to move like a robot through an obstacle course. The vocabulary they use is very important. The key terms are: turn in the terms of right angles for quarter, half and three-quarter turns, clockwise and anticlockwise, forwards, backwards, left and right.

- It is important to be strict when it comes to the instructions that children should give. 'Walk forwards' and 'Turn right' are too vague as there is no indication of the distance the robot should walk or how many quarter turns should be made. These commands should be 'Walk forwards four steps' and 'Make a right-angled

turn (one quarter turn) to the right (clockwise)'. Precise language will make the activity work properly and will show children that working systematically with carefully chosen language will ensure that the robot responds correctly.

- It is equally important that the robot follows the exact instructions that the 'programmer' gives them, even if they think that they are incorrect. For instance, if the programmer incorrectly says 'anticlockwise' rather than 'clockwise', the robot should follow the incorrect instruction (rather than what they know to be the intended one) so that the programmer can see the error and correct it.

Launching the activity

1. Show poster 16b of shapes with right angles. Create four stations around the classroom and label them: 0 right angles, 1 right angle, 2 right angles, 3 or more right angles.

2. Ask: *What does a right angle look like?* Remind them that it is a quarter turn or compare it to the corners of a square.

3. As you point to a shape on the poster, children should move to the station that they think is the answer to 'How many right angles does this shape have?' Repeat for all the shapes.

4. Display pictures of different sorts of robots around the classroom, e.g. including robots that build cars, are used in factories and from space missions.

5. Give the children two minutes to look at the pictures and share their conjectures about them. Ask: *What's the same? What's different about these pictures?* Establish that they are all pictures of robots. Stress that robots only do what they are told to do. They do not think for themselves.

6. Share the main poster and discuss.

7. Role model with another adult or confident child how the activity works.
   - Give one simple instruction at a time.
   - Each instruction should be either a movement forwards or backwards, or either a clockwise or anticlockwise turn.
   - Each instruction should include a number of steps, or amount of turn to be made.
   - Finish the set of instructions by reaching a designated area of the classroom or by having the robot pick up an identified object.

8. With children in mixed-ability pairs, give them 20 minutes to take their robot on a journey around the classroom (or outside if appropriate). Reinforce the importance of the language.

9. Regroup the children and invite a confident pair to demonstrate their work. The programmer should whisper the instructions to the robot. Ask the remaining children, *What do you think the instruction was? How do you know?*

Developing reasoning

➤ ***What do you notice*** about the shapes on the poster?
➤ Which right angled shape is the ***odd one out***? Why?
➤ ***What's the same? What's different*** about the robots?
➤ What instruction do you think the programmer just whispered to their robot? How do you know?

Providing differentiation

Support
Give the children cards with simple instructions on as a prompt to support their use of the language.

Extension
Encourage children to use three-quarter turns to make a quarter turn in the opposite direction, i.e. for a quarter turn clockwise, use a three-quarter turn anticlockwise. This can then be extended to 180, 270 and 360 degree turns.

 Key strategies

7 Odd one out
10 What do you notice?
12 What's the same? What's different?

 Problem-solving approaches

Mixed-ability pairs

Taking it further

Encourage children to play this game in the playground. It will reinforce the learning and will be fun to play as well. They could also design a short obstacle course to guide a programmable toy.

17 Fruit bowl challenge

Learning objective
- To interpret and construct simple pictograms.
- To ask and answer questions about totalling and comparing categorical data.

Reasoning skills
- Solving problems
- Conjecturing and convincing
- Making comparisons

Curriculum link
- **x=** Statistics: interpret pictograms

The problem

Problem 17

Fruit bowl challenge

Ahmed likes apples, Benji likes bananas, Clara likes cherries and Dieter likes damsons.

What is your class's favourite fruit?

How could we find out?

What questions could we ask?

What would you do if Edie, Francesca and Geraint joined the class?

Things to think about

- How many people does each picture represent?
- How will the extra children affect the pictogram?
- Which questions will tell the story of the data?

Your challenge

Find out everyone's favourite fruit, then write some questions for a friend to answer.
Show the data if one picture equals 2 children.
Think of a question about the data that no one else will ask.

Remember: You need to know what one picture equals on a pictogram.
Is it one person, two or more?
Ask questions that show the differences between sets of data and totals of amounts.

RISING STARS
Maths

Year 2

Problem Solving and Reasoning

Background knowledge

- The children create a pictogram from collected data and set questions on it. It is important that the picture used to represent the data is consistently the same image and the same size. To achieve this, provide standardised pieces of paper to draw on. For different fruits, they should draw stick men (boys/girls) to represent themselves rather than drawing fruit; however, the pieces of paper that the images are drawn on should be identical. Sticky notes work well for this.
- In the most simple form of a pictogram, one picture should represent one piece of data. As children's understanding increases, each picture can be used to represent 2 or more children. If the picture represents 2 children,

then half a picture would represent 1 child.
- Children should be encouraged to interpret the data with questions such as:
  - *How many more children liked bananas than apples?*
  - *Which fruit was liked by 4 children ?*
  - *How would you add the extra children to the pictogram?*
  - *If the picture represented 3 children, how would you show that 2 people like pineapples?*
  - *How many children are in the class?*
- Ensuring that children are able to adapt the pictogram to incorporate the new children is a good way of assessing whether they understand how to represent data in a pictogram.

Launching the activity

1. Mark out an x axis and a y axis on the floor of the classroom with masking tape. Make labels with the names of different animals and place them as labels along the x axis. One by one, ask children which animal is their favourite, then ask them to sit on the pictogram in the correct place for their preferred animal. Stress each time that the child is sitting in the right place for their choice of animal and that one child represents one child's choice. Ask: *Why has Jack sat next to the label 'dog'?*

2. When all the children are on the pictogram, ask a few questions to interpret the data.

3. Share the poster and discuss the problem. *How could we find out what the class's favourite fruit is?* Elicit that asking each child and creating either a table or a pictogram would be the best way.

4. Give out a sticky note to each child. Generate a list of five or six fruits that children might prefer. Ask them to draw themselves on the sticky note, taking up the whole size of the note.

5. Encourage the children to build a pictogram on a large piece of paper with the sticky notes.

6. Display the pictogram and challenge the children to come up with questions about the data. Remind them of the challenge to come up with a question that no one else has thought of.

7. Use a mini-plenary to introduce some pretend new children to the class. Ask: *What will we have to do to the pictogram to include these new children?*

8. Finally, show children the pictograms on Resource sheet 17.1, Pictograms. The first picture shows one apple representing one child, while the second shows one apple representing two children. Ask, *What's the same? What's different about the pictograms? What do you notice about the two pictograms?*

Developing reasoning

➤ *__What do you notice__ about the two pictograms?*
➤ *__What's the same? What's different__ about the two pictograms?*
➤ *If you add in two more children, how will it affect the pictogram?*
➤ *Ask your friend a question about the data? __Another, another, another.__*

Providing differentiation

Support
Provide children with cards with parts of questions on, such as 'How many … ?', ' … most popular?', '… least popular?'

Extension
Ask the children if they can re-draw the pictogram to show how it would look if one picture represented two children?

 Key strategies

2 Another, another, another
7 Odd one out
10 What do you notice?
12 What's the same? What's different?

 Problem-solving approaches

Same ability pairs
Mixed-ability pairs

Taking it further

Have class surveys running through the week.

Learning objective
- To compare, order and use place value to investigate a number square.

Reasoning skills
- Solving problems
- Making comparisons
- Using numerical reasoning
- Spotting patterns and relationships
- Working systematically

Curriculum link
1.3 Number and place value: recognise place value in digits

The problem

Problem 18a

Number square investigation

1 to 100 number squares are really useful things.

You can use them for spotting patterns in numbers, for doing calculations and counting up and down.

Have you ever looked closely at a 1 to 100 square?

How many 1s do you need to make a 1 to 100 square?

How many 2s, 3s, 4s etc.?

Things to think about

- Which numbers have a 0 in?
- Which numbers do you need a 0 for?
- What about a 101 to 200 square?

Your challenge

Investigate a 1 to 100 square.
Work out how many of each digit are needed for the square.
Estimate first.
How close to your estimate is your answer?

Remember: Work systematically. Start at 1 and check every number up to 100.
You only need a 0 for some of the numbers.
For every ten numbers, you only need a 7 once (except for the 70s).

Year 2

Problem Solving and Reasoning

Background knowledge

- The children are asked to investigate squares with one hundred numbers. 1–100 squares are often just called 'hundred squares'. This can be misleading as although they do represent 100 numbers, it does not state which 100 numbers. A 'hundred square' could be 101–200 or 201–300. In this problem, children should start with a 1–100 square and move on to a 101–200 sqaure as an extension. Of course, a hundred square could start at any number, e.g. 15–114.

- Estimating the total number of digits required to make a 1–100 square before the activity will encourage children to visualise the different parts of the square as they make their estimation. This visualisation is an important stage in the forming of a child's internal representation of a 1–100 square.

- The digit 1 is used to make the numbers 12, 31 and 100, as well as the number 1. It is not the number 1 that is used.

Launching the activity

1. Start with a counting activity. Introduce the idea of changing direction. Count round a circle in ones. When the adult says, *Change!*, the next child should start counting down instead of up. Keep going until a child says *100*.

2. Display poster 18b and give children five seconds to look at it. Then cover it and ask questions such as: *Which number comes after 16? Which number comes before 51? On a 1–100 square, which number would you find beneath the number 45/find above the number 90? How would you find the number that is 10 more than 67? How many 1s (as a digit) are there on the top row of the 1–100 square?*

3. Share the main poster and ensure the children understand the difference between the number 1 and the digit 1.

4. Give out sticky notes to each child. Ask them to 'think, pair share' the number of each digit that they will need to make a 1–100 square.

5. After their estimates, give them 10 sticky notes and set them the challenge of working out how many of each digit they would need to make a 1–100 square, recording their solutions on the sticky notes (one digit per sticky note).

6. Use a mini-plenary to look at a 1–100 square on poster 18b. Ask: *What patterns can you see in the square?* Highlight all of the numbers that end in 6, (6, 16, 26, 36 ...) *What do you notice? Do any other numbers have a 6 in them? How many 6s do you need in total?*

7. Regroup the children and share their solutions. Compare their solutions to their estimates.

8. Count up as a class how many of each digit that you need to make the 1–100 square.

Developing reasoning

➤ *How many 6s do you need in total? Can you link this to any other digits?*
➤ ***What do you notice*** *about the pattern of the numbers with a 6 in?*
➤ *How are the numbers 1–9 the* **same** *as or* **different** *from the numbers 21–29?*
➤ *If you need 21 ones between 1 and 100, how many would you need between 101 and 200?*

Providing differentiation

Support
Have a 1–100 square available to support children as required. This will remove some of the visualisation of the 1–100 square, but will support those children who cannot visualise it.

Reduce the range of numbers that the children have to investigate. Ask instead: *How many of each digit do you need to make the numbers between 1 and 20 on a number line?*

Extension
Ask children: *If you know that you need 19 sixes in a 1–100 square, how could you work out how many sevens you would need without counting them up?*

How many ones would you need to make a 101–200 square?

 Key strategies

10 What do you notice?
12 What's the same? What's different?

 Problem-solving approaches

Think, pair, share
Working in pairs

Taking it further

Give the children this challenge: *If you are making a number line out of halves from 0–10 ($\frac{1}{2}$, 1, 1$\frac{1}{2}$, 2, 2$\frac{1}{2}$ etc.), how many ones would you need?*

Glossary

Commutative An operation which can be carried out in any order without affecting the result. Addition and multiplication are commutative, e.g. $4 \times 3 = 3 \times 4$ and $8 + 7 = 7 + 8$.

Conjecture A thought or idea about a pattern, solution or relationship. Children should be encouraged to form conjectures about maths, e.g. 'My conjecture is that the answer will always be a product of the other numbers' and then to convince themselves and their peers that their conjecture is true.

Denominator The bottom number in a fraction. This shows how many equal parts the whole is split into.

Digit Digits are 0, 1, 2, 3, 4, 5, 6, 7, 8, 9. Their position within a number determines their value.

Digit root The number formed when continuously finding the digit sum until a single digit number is formed, e.g. the digit root of 789 is 6 ($7 + 8 + 9 = 24$, $2 + 4 = 6$).

Digit sum The number formed when all the digits in a number are added (as if each digit were in the ones place), e.g. the digit sum of 789 is 24 ($7 + 8 + 9$).

Factor Factors of a number are numbers which multiply together to give that number and usually come in pairs, e.g. the factors of 24 are 1 and 24, 2 and 12, 3 and 8, 4 and 6.

Fraction A way of showing a proportion of a whole. Fractions take the form ½ and are made up of a numerator and denominator. A fraction splits the whole into equal parts.

Multiple A number which can be divided by another number without leaving a remainder, e.g. 6 is a multiple of 360 as $360 \div 6 = 60$.

Number Numbers are digits which have been assigned a place value, e.g. the digits 3, 5 and 6 can be arranged to make the number 563 with the digit 5 having a value of 500 or 5 hundreds, the digit 6 having the value of 60 or 6 tens and the digit 3 having the value of 3 or 3 ones.

Numerator The top number in a fraction. This shows how many of the equal parts you 'have'.

Partitioning Breaking up a number into smaller numbers. Partitioning can be canonical, which means breaking multiples of 10, 100, 1000, etc (e.g. 878 partitioned canonically would be $800 + 70 + 8$, or $400 + 400 + 70 + 8$) or non-canonically which means partitioning into numbers which are not all multiples of 10, 100, 1000, etc (e.g. $878 = 450 + 350 + 35 + 35 + 6 + 2$).

Polygon An enclosed shape with 3 or more straight sides. Regular polygons have equal sides and angles. Irregular polygons are those where the sides and angles differ in size.

Prime Prime numbers have only two factors: 1 and the number itself.

Product The result when multiplying two or more numbers together, e.g. the product of 3, 4 and 2 is 24.

Quadrilateral A 4-sided polygon.

Rectangle A quadrilateral with 4 right angles and 2 pairs of equal and parallel sides. A square is a special type of rectangle with 4 equal sides.

Square numbers Square numbers have an odd number of factors, as they can be formed by multiplying a number by itself, e.g. 16 is a square number, as it is the product of 4×4.

Sum The total when adding two or more numbers together, e.g. the sum of $5 + 6$ is 11. 'Sums' do not refer to any type of calculation other than addition.

Systematically The act of working in an ordered and considered way, especially when tackling a problem or investigation, e.g. when exploring numbers which sum to 100, a systematic way of working would be to start with $100 + 0$, then $99 + 1$, $98 + 2$, $97 + 3$, etc.